W9-BJR-817

# THE CLOISTERS

ARCADES AND GARDEN COURT OF THE CUXA CLOISTER

THE METROPOLITAN MUSEUM
OF ART

# THE CLOISTERS

THE BUILDING AND THE
COLLECTION OF MEDIAE-
VAL ART · IN FORT TRYON
PARK · BY JAMES J. RORIMER
NEW YORK · MCMLI

# PREFACE TO THE FIRST EDITION

IN 1925 John D. Rockefeller, Jr., presented to The Metropolitan Museum of Art a sum of money with which to purchase and maintain the collection of mediaeval sculpture and architectural material assembled by George Grey Barnard and since 1914 open to the public in a brick structure built especially for it on Fort Washington Avenue.

The Barnard collection was perhaps the most extensive of its kind in America at that time. Both the way in which it was brought together and the manner in which it was displayed were remarkable achievements of enthusiasm and industry on the part of a single individual. Large sections of the cloisters of the long abandoned and ruined monasteries of Saint-Michel-de-Cuxa, Saint-Guilhem-le-Désert, Bonnefont-en-Comminges, and Trie formed the nucleus of a collection in which there had been brought together such notable pieces of mediaeval sculpture as the tomb effigy of Jean d'Alluye, a Romanesque torso of the crucified Christ, wooden figures of Mary and John from a thirteenth-century Crucifixion group, and numerous statues of the Virgin from the Île-de-France and Lorraine.

When in 1926 the collection was rearranged and the building reopened as a branch of the Metropolitan Museum and called The Cloisters, Mr. and Mrs. Rockefeller added some forty more sculptures from their private collection, and two years later Mr. Rockefeller presented the great tomb of Count Armengol VII.

From time to time, during the succeeding ten years, Mr. Rockefeller has given other important mediaeval monuments to the collection, but for the exhibition of most of these additional gifts the original structure was wholly inadequate. Therefore, when in June, 1930, he presented to the City the

v

high land overlooking the Hudson which is now Fort Tryon Park, he reserved the northern hilltop for a new and larger Cloisters museum, the design of which he entrusted to Charles Collens of the firm of Allen, Collens and Willis of Boston. In planning the installation of the objects in the old Cloisters which were to be shown with the later acquisitions in the new, Joseph Breck, Assistant Director of the Metropolitan Museum, worked in collaboration with Mr. Collens. Upon Mr. Breck's death in 1933 this responsibility fell to James J. Rorimer, who had been closely associated with him in the Museum since 1927 and who became Curator of the Department of Mediaeval Art on January 1, 1934, and of The Cloisters on January 1, 1938. Throughout the period of actual construction, which began in 1934, Mr. Collens and Mr. Rorimer have been in intimate co-operation, and to these two more than to anyone else the present form of The Cloisters is due. The Committee on the Buildings, under the chairmanship of William Church Osborn, has had general oversight of the undertaking for the Trustees, and Mr. Rockefeller has followed every detail with the deepest interest.

The objects presented during the last ten years by Mr. Rockefeller are now shown for the first time in the new Cloisters and add immeasurably to the interest of the collection. To select but a few, there are the Spanish thirteenth-century Adoration group from Cerezo de Riotirón and the frescoes from the chapter house of the monastery of San Pedro de Arlanza; the chapter house from the twelfth-century French abbey at Pontaut; the great sculptured doorway from the thirteenth-century French abbey at Moutiers-Saint-Jean; and a magnificent fourteenth-century statue of the Virgin and Child from the Île-de-France. But of all the great works of art now in The Cloisters, perhaps precedence should be given to the famous fifteenth-century French or Flemish tapestries

# PREFACE

depicting The Hunt of the Unicorn—the outstanding set of Gothic tapestries in this country.

To the original Cloisters collection and to the incomparable additions made to it by Mr. Rockefeller, further additions have come as gifts from other friends of the Museum and through purchase. George Blumenthal has presented ten twelfth-century corbels, a twelfth-century doorway from Reugny, four fifteenth-century windows from Sens, and a contemporary arcade from the priory at Froville. Stephen C. Clark presented three of the capitals from Trie. With income from the Rogers Fund the Museum has purchased parts of the choir of the twelfth-century church at Langon now installed in the Romanesque Chapel.

From the collections in the main building of the Metropolitan Museum there have been moved to The Cloisters a number of objects, of which perhaps the most notable are the twelfth-century Spanish crucifix, the thirteenth-century lion from Zamora and portal from Frías, and the fifteenth-century ceiling from Illescas.

H. E. WINLOCK

*May,* 1938

# PREFACE TO THE ELEVENTH EDITION

THIS book was first published in May 1938 and has been reprinted nine times with minor changes. This edition, the eleventh, has been extensively revised and enlarged to include all the major acquisitions for the collections and changes in the building that have been made in recent years. The enrichment of The Cloisters has been made possible through the continued guidance and substantial funds provided by John D. Rockefeller, Jr. The Heroes tapestries, the chalice of Antioch and other objects for the Treasury, three Catalan tombs, the Strasbourg Virgin, about twenty other sculptures, and furniture and paintings have been purchased. Many of these objects were selected from the private collection of the late Joseph Brummer.

Among the many who have given assistance in the preparation of this book are Margaret B. Freeman and William H. Forsyth, Associate Curators, Vera K. Ostoia, Junior Research Fellow, Bonnie Young, Assistant, and Agnes Peters, Associate Editor, whose devoted help has been of inestimable value.

JAMES J. RORIMER
*Director of The Cloisters*

*June,* 1951

# CONTENTS

PREFACE TO THE FIRST EDITION *page* v

PREFACE TO THE ELEVENTH EDITION viii

CONTENTS ix

ILLUSTRATIONS xi

INTRODUCTION xvii

THE MIDDLE AGES IN FRANCE AND SPAIN xvii

THE CHURCH xxii

MONASTICISM IN WESTERN EUROPE xxiii

THE MONASTERY xxvii

THE BUILDING, LANDSCAPING, AND GARDENS

   OF THE CLOISTERS xxxi

SUGGESTED ITINERARY xxxvi

## THE CLOISTERS

THE ROMANESQUE HALL 1

THE SAINT-GUILHEM CLOISTER 16

THE ROMANESQUE CHAPEL 22

THE CHAPTER HOUSE FROM PONTAUT 33

THE CUXA CLOISTER 38

THE NINE HEROES TAPESTRY ROOM 47

THE EARLY GOTHIC HALL 56

THE GOTHIC CHAPEL                          *page* 65

THE BONNEFONT CLOISTER                          81

THE TRIE CLOISTER                               85

THE FIFTEENTH-CENTURY SCULPTURE HALL            90

THE TREASURY                                    99

THE BOPPARD ROOM                               115

THE HALL OF THE UNICORN TAPESTRIES             120

THE BURGOS TAPESTRY HALL                       135

THE SPANISH ROOM                               139

THE LATE GOTHIC HALL                           142

THE FROVILLE ARCADE                            153


INDEX                                          155

# ILLUSTRATIONS

*Frontispiece:* Arcades and Garden Court of the
Cuxa Cloister

Map Showing the Provenance of the Principal French
and Spanish Objects at The Cloisters     *page* xix

Plan of the Cistercian Abbey of Royaumont     xxix

Plan of the Main Floor of The Cloisters     xxxvi

Plan of the Ground Floor of The Cloisters     xxxvii

*Figures:*

1. A Lion. Fresco from San Pedro de Arlanza.
   Spanish, about 1220     2

2. The Adoration of the Magi. Sculpture from the
   Church of Nuestra Señora de la Llama, Cerezo
   de Riotirón. Spanish, about 1188     5

3. Joseph, a Figure in the Adoration Group from
   Cerezo de Riotirón     7

4. Doorway from Reugny. French, Late XII Century     8

5, 6. The Virgin and Saint John. Probably Italian,
   XIII Century     9

7. Doorway from Moutiers-Saint-Jean. Burgundian,
   XIII Century     13

8. Arcades and Court of the Saint-Guilhem Cloister     17

9. A Capital from Saint-Guilhem-le-Désert. French,
   before 1206     19

10. The Romanesque Chapel     23

# ILLUSTRATIONS

11. A Capital from Langon. French, XII Century   *page* 24

12. The Virgin and Child. Burgundian, XII Century   26

13. Crucifix. Spanish, XII Century   29

14. The Virgin (?) and a Monk. Stained Glass. French, XIII Century   31

15. The Chapter House from Notre-Dame-de-Pontaut. French, XII Century   35

16. The Interior of the Chapter House from Pontaut   36

17. A Capital from Pontaut   37

18. Part of the East Arcade of the Cuxa Cloister   39

19-22. Capitals from Saint-Michel-de-Cuxa. French, Second Half of the XII Century   43

23. King Arthur. One of the Nine Heroes Tapestries. French, Late XIV Century   49

24. Courtiers and Banners with the Duke of Berry's Arms. Detail from the Tapestry of the Hebrew Heroes   50

25. Alexander the Great (?) One of the Nine Heroes Tapestries. French, Late XIV Century   53

26. Julius Caesar. One of the Nine Heroes Tapestries. French, Late XIV Century   55

27. The Virgin from the Choir Screen of Strasbourg Cathedral. Rhenish, 1247-1252   57

28. The Virgin and Child. French (Île-de-France), XIV Century   59

29. A Bishop. Italian, XIV Century   60

# ILLUSTRATIONS

30. A Deacon Saint. French, XIV Century     *page* 61

31. The Man of Sorrows. Fresco by a Follower of
Nardo di Cione. Italian, XIV Century    62

32. The Adoration of the Shepherds. Italian, Sienese
School, XIV Century    64

33. The Sepulchral Effigy of Jean d'Alluye. French,
XIII Century    66

34. The Tomb of Don Alvaró de Cabrera. Spanish
(Catalan), 1299-1314    69

35. Tombs of Armengol X and Doña Dulcia, Wife of
Armengol VII. Spanish (Catalan), 1299-1314    70

36. The Tomb of Armengol VII, Count of Urgel.
Spanish (Catalan), 1299-1314    71

37, 38. Saint Margaret and Another Saint. Spanish,
about 1330    75

39. A Bishop. Burgundian, Early XIV Century    77

40. Lancets with Stained Glass from Évron. French,
XIV Century    78

41. Arcades of the Bonnefont Cloister    80

42, 43. Capitals from Bonnefont-en-Comminges.
French, Late XIII-Early XIV Century    83

44. Arcades and Garden Court of the Trie Cloister    87

45. A Capital from Trie. French, probably about
1484-1490    88

46. Bishop and Donor. Burgundian, XV Century    90

47. A Burgher. French, XV Century    91

48. Saint Barbara. French, XV Century     *page* 92

49. Pietà. Rhenish, about 1375-1400     93

50. Saint Hubert and the Stag. French, XVI Century     95

51-54. Stained-Glass Roundels. Flemish and German, Late XV-XVI Century     97

55. Woodwork from Abbeville. French, Late XV-Early XVI Century     98

56. Mount on One of the Doors to the Treasury. XII-XIII Century     99

57. Wood Panels with Scenes from the Life of Christ. French and Flemish, Early XVI Century     100

58. The Nativity and the Vision of the Magi. Detail from an Altarpiece by a Follower of Rogier van der Weyden. Second Half of the XV Century     101

59. The Chalice of Antioch. Early Christian, IV-V Century     103

60. Chalice. By Brother Bertinus, 1222     104

61. Chalice, Paten, and Straws. German, Second Quarter of the XIII Century     105

62. Bowl from a Ciborium. Channel School, XII Century     106

63. Reliquaries. XIII-XV Century     109

64. Candlesticks, Altar Cruet, and Eucharistic Dove. French (Limoges), XIII Century     110

65. Clasp. Style of Nicholas of Verdun. From the Region of the Meuse, about 1200     111

# ILLUSTRATIONS

66. Aquamanile. German, XII or XIII Century    *page* 112

67. Bird. German or Italian, XI-XIII Century    113

68. Covered Beakers. German (Ingolstadt), Second
    Half of the XV Century    114

69. Stained Glass from Boppard. Rhenish, Second
    Quarter of the XV Century    116

70. Alabaster Retable from the Archbishop's Palace in
    Saragossa. Spanish, XV Century    118

71. Saint Stephen. German, First Half of the XVI
    Century    119

72. The Unicorn at the Fountain. Tapestry in the
    Series Called The Hunt of the Unicorn. Franco-
    Flemish, about 1500    121

73. The Unicorn Tries to Escape. Tapestry in the
    Series Called The Hunt of the Unicorn. Franco-
    Flemish, about 1500    123

74. Detail from Figure 73    124

75. The Unicorn Defends Himself. Tapestry in the
    Series Called The Hunt of the Unicorn. Franco-
    Flemish, about 1500    127

76. The Unicorn is Brought to the Castle. Tapestry in
    the Series Called The Hunt of the Unicorn.
    Franco-Flemish, about 1500    129

77. The Unicorn in Captivity. Tapestry in the Series
    Called The Hunt of the Unicorn. Franco-
    Flemish, about 1515    131

78. Stained Glass with the Arms of the Emperor Maxi-
    milian. Flemish, about 1504-1506    133

79. Astrologers of the East; the Vision of the Magi. Detail from a Tapestry from Burgos Cathedral. Flemish (Brussels), about 1500. *page* 137

80. The Spanish Room 141

81. Doorway. French, Early XVI Century 143

82. The Baptism of Christ. Detail from Figure 83 144

83. Retable with Scenes from the Life of Saint John the Baptist. Spanish, about 1480. Probably by Francisco Solibes de Bañolas 145

84. Retable with Saint Anne and the Virgin and Child. Spanish (Aragonese), Second Half of the XV Century 149

85. The Virgin Kneeling. Italian, Early XVI Century 150

86. A View of The Cloisters, Showing Two Windows from Sens and the Froville Arcade 152

87. The View of the Hudson River and the George Washington Bridge from The Cloisters 154

# INTRODUCTION

THE MIDDLE AGES IN FRANCE AND SPAIN. The Middle Ages is the term loosely applied to the period from about the time of Constantine (311-337), the first Christian emperor, to the beginning of the Renaissance. Early in the mediaeval period the Germanic tribes were slowly adjusting their primitive cultures to that of the ancient world. By the fifth century the Roman provinces of Spain and Gaul, the Italian states, and Britain had begun to emerge as independent units. The centuries between the collapse of Roman civilization and the ephemeral Carolingian renaissance in the ninth century are often referred to as the Dark Ages. With regard to the disintegration of organized society and the decline of general culture this term aptly characterizes these years; it fails, however, to suggest the existence of such enlightened people as the comparatively few and scattered scholars, chiefly churchmen and monks, who kept alive the learning and skills inherited by Rome from Egypt and Greece.

Charlemagne, who was crowned emperor by Pope Leo III at Rome in 800, promoted education and revived learning. Later in the ninth century, however, his innovations were checked by a breakdown of government caused by dissensions among his descendants. By the treaty of Mersen, in 870, three states, the West Frankish kingdom, the East Frankish kingdom, and the kingdom of Italy, were established. The history of the West Frankish kingdom and of its southern neighbor, Spain, is of particular interest in view of the provenance of most of the exhibits in The Cloisters (see map, p. xix).

The West Frankish kingdom, which for our purposes may henceforth be called France, comprised somewhat the same territory as modern France and Belgium. The land was given in grants to rival dukes and counts, who through a complicated system of vassalage owed allegiance to the king. As each sought to extend his influence through force they constantly engaged in warfare. In the tenth century Normandy, Brittany, Flanders, and Burgundy became powerful feudal estates under hereditary lords. In the eleventh century the French kings were continually involved in strife with their vassals, but added little to the prestige of the crown. Duke William of Normandy, a vassal of the King of France, invaded England and, after defeating Harold the Saxon at the battle of Hastings in 1066, had himself made king. Recurrent wars with the English, the result of the Norman invasion, were to be the chief concern of France and the French kings until almost the end of the Middle Ages. At the close of the eleventh century armies led by Count Raymond of Toulouse, Duke Godfrey of Bouillon, and other nobles set out on the first crusade to rescue the Holy Land from the Turks. The capture of Jerusalem in 1099 established close commercial relations between the East and the West.

Abbot Suger of Saint-Denis, minister to Louis VI (1108-1137) and regent while Louis VII (1137-1180) was away on the second crusade, was largely responsible for the encouragement given to the arts during these reigns. The Paris schools of learning flourished under the leadership of able teachers, of whom the most famous was Abelard (died in 1142). In this period which is appropriately known as the twelfth-century renaissance the Romanesque style reached its fullest development, and Gothic art had begun to evolve. Philip II (1180-1223), called Philip Augustus and "the founder of Paris," rebuilt the Louvre, which later kings enlarged, and granted the first extant charter of privileges to the University of Paris, one of the oldest of modern universities. More than sixteen cathedrals were begun in his reign.

When Philip ascended the throne, Henry II (1154-1189),

MAP SHOWING THE PROVENANCE OF THE PRINCIPAL FRENCH
AND SPANISH OBJECTS AT THE CLOISTERS

a great-grandson of William the Conqueror, was not only King of England but Duke of Normandy, suzerain of Brittany, and Count of Anjou and Maine; and by marriage with Eleanor of Aquitaine he had doubled his vast French domains (see p. 24). Eventually Philip succeeded in reducing substantially the amount of French territory that English kings controlled as feudal lords. He accompanied Richard the Lion-hearted to the East in 1190, on the third crusade, but took no active part in the crusade proclaimed in 1208 by Pope Innocent III against the Albigensian heretics (see p. 16), a sect that had gained a large following in southern France.

The reign of Louis IX (1226-1270), better known as Saint Louis, may be called the golden age of mediaeval France. At this time some of the greatest monuments of France, such as the cathedral of Notre-Dame at Paris, were completed, and that jewel of architecture, the Sainte-Chapelle, was built. The illuminated manuscripts made for the king and his mother, Blanche of Castile, and the great series of stained-glass windows created in his reign exemplify the perfection attained in the arts. An agreement which Saint Louis made with the King of Aragon in 1258 is of interest for the glimpse it gives of the history of the region from which the Cuxa Cloister and other works of art in the collection came. On condition that the King of Aragon abandon claims to parts of Provence and Languedoc, the French king relinquished claims to Roussillon and Barcelona which dated back to the time of Charlemagne.

For almost two hundred years after the reign of Louis IX France lived through perilous times. Philip IV (1285-1314), called "the Fair," engaged in a historic controversy with Pope Boniface VIII over the question of taxation of the clergy; this was won by the king with the support of the Estates General, a parliamentary body which he assembled in 1302. The Black Death, the bubonic plague of 1348, brought terrible sufferings to France, as to all Europe. From 1337 until 1453 the Hundred Years' War with England was waged intermittently; at the close the English lost to Charles VII (1422-1461) the last of their possessions in southern France and the prestige of the French crown emerged from eclipse. In this period the affluence and power of the nobles and burghers began to grow, and were increasingly reflected in the arts.

Under Louis XI (1461-1483) the consolidation of France was practically completed, for in 1482 Burgundy came under the sway of the central authority. The marriage of Charles VIII (1483-1498) to Anne of Brittany brought another important duchy into union with the French crown. In 1493, by the treaty of Barcelona, Charles ceded to Spain the territory of Roussillon, which had been pawned to France in 1462.

After Charles's invasion of Italy in 1494, changes began to take place in the cultural life of France. Although for a few more years French art belonged to the Middle Ages, it soon felt the influences of the Italian Renaissance. In international affairs the modern world had already commenced. The Turks had taken Constantinople, the Moors had been crushed in Spain, and Columbus had discovered America. Before long reflections of exploration in the East and in the West, as well as in the sciences and other fields of learning, appeared in the art of France.

IN the Middle Ages practically all of the Spanish peninsula fell into the possession of Muhammadans from northern Africa, who first invaded the country in 711. In the next five centuries, however, there developed, in northern Spain, independent kingdoms—Castile and León, Aragon, and Navarre —whose rulers eventually reconquered most of the lost territory. But Spain did not become an important power in Europe until the country was consolidated through the marriage of

Ferdinand of Aragon and Isabella of Castile in 1469. The art of northern Spain, which emanated largely from the Church and its monasteries, was affected comparatively little by the great Moorish culture established, particularly in the south, under the Caliphate of Cordova.

THE CHURCH. The most powerful institution, either temporal or spiritual, in the Middle Ages was the Roman Catholic Church. From the time of Constantine until the Reformation it claimed the allegiance of Christendom in western Europe.

The clergy, who administered the Church, were organized in a hierarchical system, which included archbishops, bishops, parish priests, and deacons, all finally responsible to the pope, the Bishop of Rome. The Church accumulated vast domains and other wealth. Through gifts and tithes it became the richest institution of mediaeval times. Through a combination of spiritual authority and material power its activities were more widespread and more far-reaching than those of the Holy Roman Empire or any of the European kingdoms.

Stories from the Old and the New Testament and from accounts of the lives of the saints were used to illustrate and to teach the doctrines of the Church. The stories provided instances of exemplary conduct and, often, of miraculous incident. They were treated extensively in the literature of Europe and were repeated again and again in art.

That the Church found art a helpful handmaid in the work it set out to accomplish is confirmed by noble testimony from the past. When the Church was at the peak of its power in the twelfth and thirteenth centuries, mediaeval architecture and the related arts were at their height. The works of mediaeval art which still survive, from the greatest cathedrals to the smallest hermitages, are evidence of the devout spirit in which they were conceived. With the increase of strength and independence in national governments and the changes which came with the Reformation, the power of the Catholic Church was curtailed. At this time artists were already beginning to work more and more for nobles and wealthy burghers, and even ecclesiastical art was influenced by the awakening of the dormant traditions of classical Greece and Rome.

MONASTICISM IN WESTERN EUROPE. Monasticism is not confined to Christianity. Groups which lived in seclusion and practiced asceticism existed before the time of Christ, among them the Buddhist monks in India, the Essenes in Judea, and the Therapeutae in Egypt, near Alexandria. To what extent any of these pre-Christian sects influenced the development of Christian monasticism is uncertain, but it is clear that the Christian institution was not an imitation or an adaptation of any earlier form.

Christian monasticism, which appears in Egypt about the beginning of the fourth century, is generally believed to be a way of life first adopted by Saint Anthony (about 250-about 355). Thousands, emulating him, became hermits and retired to the desert to dwell alone or in groups, devoting themselves to religious exercises. His disciples transmitted his principles by oral instruction and example, and in this way a mode of ascetic life that was wholly individualistic in emphasis was established. The Antonian precedent later prevailed in eastern Europe. Cenobitical monasticism, a form that took its name from the cenobium, or community, in which a group of men or women gathered to share a life dedicated to a religious ideal, was introduced about 315 or 320 by Saint Pachomius (about 290-346). More practical than Saint Anthony, he provided his followers with a written rule, or code of discipline, and required each member of the community to engage in some active and

# INTRODUCTION

constructive work suited to his talents. He also originated the
religious order, an association of monastic communities that
functioned under the supervision of the superior of the chief
monastery, by whom the heads of the subordinate houses were
nominated. It is interesting to note that the idea of conduct-
ing monasteries under a centralized administration was not
put into practice again until the foundation of the Cluniac
order in the tenth century (see p. xxvi) and that the preroga-
tives exercised by the Pachomian superiors foreshadowed the
rights accorded to abbots in certain orders in the Middle Ages.

The most important figure in the development of monasticism in western Europe was Saint Benedict of Nursia (about
480-543), who devised a rule which effectively adapted the
practice of monasticism to the European climate and tempera-
ment. He also founded fourteen monasteries, the most famous
being the one established about 520 at Monte Cassino.

For centuries Saint Benedict's Rule was the basis for cenobitical monasticism in Europe. The prologue states the purpose
of the work, and in the following seventy-three chapters treats
such matters as the general duties of abbots and monks, the
order of worship at divine services, the penalties to be imposed
on faults, the internal administration of a monastery, the
reception of guests, the conduct of monks when traveling,
and conditions for admission to the brotherhood. The abbot
was elected by the monks for life and governed with full
authority. He was advised to seek the opinion of the monks
before deciding important problems, but he was account-
able for his acts only to God on the Day of Judgment. The
monks were instructed to obey not only their abbot but one
another. They were expected to perform, according to their
talents and abilities, a variety of services. Their occupations,
and the total time allotted to each on an average summer day,
have been outlined as follows: religious devotions (night vigil

xxiv

and offices said at the seven canonical hours between dawn and dusk), known as the Opus Dei and considered the most important phase of monastic life, three and a half hours; solitary meditation, half an hour; reading, four hours; manual work, six and a half hours; sleep, eight and a half hours; and meals, one hour.

The Rule did not establish an order in the usual sense of the term (see pp. xxvi f.), for each monastery was independent. But in time the autonomy of the houses was modified: about the tenth century several of the greater abbeys established dependent houses; in the tenth and eleventh centuries the influence of Cluny and Cîteaux led to voluntary unions of houses observing the same rule; and in the thirteenth century the Benedictine abbeys in the various ecclesiastical provinces were required to form federations, called congregations.

The Rule of Saint Benedict has been considered as important as the constitution of any temporal state, and of all literature, it has been said, it was second only to the Bible in its influence. Many Benedictine monks were called from their life of retirement into the world. No less than twenty-four had become popes, 7,000 archbishops, and 15,000 bishops by the beginning of the fourteenth century.

At first Benedictine monasticism in France existed side by side with two other forms, the Antonian and the Irish, but gradually supplanted them. The former had been introduced by Saint Athanasius into Gaul in the fourth century, and the latter was brought to France by Saint Columbanus in the sixth century. Just when Benedictine influence was beginning to lag, it was given new vitality by Witiza of Aquitaine (died in 822), a monk who took the name of Benedict and in 779 established the monastery of Aniane. He introduced reforms which were based on the Rule and, with the support of Louis the Pious, endeavored to enforce them so that there might be uniformity of practice in all Frankish monasteries under the Benedictine Rule.

The foundation of the abbey of Cluny in 910 marked the establishment of the first of the great orders which became so influential later in the Middle Ages and which were largely responsible for the achievements in church building. It was the object of the Cluniac order to ensure uniform preservation of the Benedictine ideal by setting up a centralized organization for the government of monasteries. At the height of its power in the twelfth century the order controlled more than three hundred monasteries in France, Italy, Germany, and Spain. By the beginning of the thirteenth century the order had become too unwieldy for efficient administration by the abbot of Cluny, and a system of provincial regulation was instituted. Since its reforms met with general favor, the order accumulated enormous wealth. Subsequently it relaxed in its observance of the Rule.

From about 1125 to 1225 the Cistercian order, which had been founded at the abbey of Cîteaux in 1098, was the spiritual leader of European monasticism. It was the intention of the order to follow to the letter the Rule of Saint Benedict and to make its interpretation more rigid by applying some of the tenets of Benedict of Aniane. The Cistercian method of government is described in the *Charta charitatis*, a work by Stephen Harding which has been called the "spiritual mirror of the feudal system." The Cistercians granted the dependent monasteries greater freedom in the management of their own affairs than the Cluniac order permitted but required the abbots to assemble annually at Cîteaux. Saint Bernard (1090 1153), founder of the famous Cistercian abbey of Clairvaux, did much through his writings and teachings to reform monastic life.

Contemplative orders—the Camaldolese and the Vallombrosans in Italy and the Carthusians in France—were formed in the tenth and eleventh centuries. Their mode of life tended toward the eremitical, emphasizing strongly the Antonian rather than the Benedictine ideal.

Other ecclesiastical orders, also, appeared during the Middle Ages: the Augustinian canons, Premonstratensians, Franciscans, Dominicans, Carmelites, and military orders such as the Knights Hospitalers of Saint John, the Knights Templars, and the Teutonic Knights. But these were not strictly speaking monastic, for although their members followed a rule, the work they performed was chiefly carried on outside of monasteries, in the secular world. Towards the end of the thirteenth century monasticism declined, and by the time of the Reformation the institution had lost its great power.

T HE MONASTERY. In all western European monasteries the most important buildings were grouped around a central cloister, an open court with a covered and arcaded passageway along the sides.

There have been various suggestions as to the origin of this arrangement. It has been thought that the form of the western monastery with its central cloister was derived from the East. In Syria it was customary to place an atrium, or court, in front of the main entrance or at one side of a church and to construct buildings around it, with porticoes, usually arcaded, extended along the sides. The cloister at Bābiskā in Syria, with two porticoes dating from 401, is considered by some scholars to be the earliest known cloister. Since there were western monks who had lived in eastern monasteries, it is possible that some of them may have introduced these ideas into western monastic architecture.

It has also been thought that the plan of western monasteries was suggested by that of Roman houses, whose principal rooms were built around a colonnaded inner court, called the peristyle. Early Christian literature furnishes records of the conversion of such houses into monasteries. In the *Acta Sanctorum*, for example, Saint Aglaë tells of rich Romans who became monks and gave their houses to be used as monasteries, and similar reports are made by Saint Jerome. Such incidents also occurred outside of Rome. At Trier (Trèves) the house of Tetradius became the monastery of Saint Martin about 406.

The development of monastic architecture in Europe was influenced by the Rule of Saint Benedict, which stated that a monastery should provide every requirement for monastic life. Therefore monasteries included all the buildings necessary for the various activities of the monks. The widespread influence of Benedictinism is apparent in the monastic buildings represented in The Cloisters collections. Saint-Guilhem-le-Désert, Notre-Dame-de-la-Grande-Sauve, Notre-Dame-de-Langon, Saint-Michel-de-Cuxa, Pontaut (governed by the Cistercians after 1151), and Froville were all built by Benedictines, and Bonnefont-en-Comminges was built by Cistercians.

Unfortunately no Benedictine monasteries dating from Saint Benedict's lifetime are in existence today. The monastery of Jumièges in northern France is believed to have been among the first in France to observe, though probably only in part, the Benedictine Rule. The original buildings and the cloister, erected just after 650, when Benedictine influence was taking hold in Gaul, were destroyed in the ninth century; but they are described in considerable detail in the *Vita Sancti Philiberti*, written about 750. In Spain a few monastic buildings dating from the ninth and tenth centuries survive, but most of the important ones now extant date from the twelfth century or later.

The oldest existing plan of a monastery, drawn on parchment about 830, is preserved at the abbey of Saint-Gall in Switzerland. The buildings are represented in great detail, and

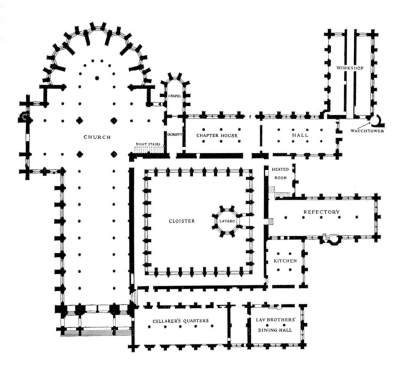

PLAN OF THE CISTERCIAN ABBEY OF ROYAUMONT

many of their features are typical of monasteries built in the ensuing centuries. To illustrate the principal characteristics of mediaeval monasteries, the plan of the abbey of Royaumont is reproduced on page xxix. It shows clearly the various elements of a monastery in the most usual arrangement. The abbey was founded in the thirteenth century by the French king Saint Louis and was built by the Cistercians. This order was among the great monastic builders of the Middle Ages.

Most of the monks' activities, other than those of worship, centered in the cloister. It was there that they walked in solemn meditation and on occasion were permitted to talk informally (formal discussion of problems took place in the chapter house). In the cloister they had their school, studied, and copied manuscripts. The cloisters of western European monasteries were approximately rectangular in shape. Instead of being placed in front of the church, as were the atria of Early Christian basilicas, the cloister was always at one side, preferably the south, and usually in the angle formed by one of the arms of the transept and the nave. One of the walks of the cloister was next to the wall of the nave. The chief building on the opposite walk, facing the church, was the refectory. The chapter house and sometimes the sacristy and the armarium (library) adjoined the transept. The cloister side of the chapter house was almost always open, as at Pontaut (see pp. 33 ff.), although occasionally in northern countries, owing to the cold, it was enclosed. The dormitory was on the second floor, preferably over the chapter house so that the monks could readily reach the church by the night stairs. On the fourth side there were storerooms (the cellarer's quarters) and workshops. Some very large monasteries, for instance the great Cistercian abbey of Clairvaux, had several cloisters, as numerous buildings were necessary to serve the complex requirements of a large community.

THE BUILDING, LANDSCAPING, AND GAR-
DENS OF THE CLOISTERS. The purpose of
The Cloisters, as expressed by the donor, is to provide a culmi-
nating point of interest in the architectural design of Fort
Tryon Park and also to house properly and display to advan-
tage the various collections described in the following pages.

The building (see cover) is not copied from any mediaeval building, nor is it a composite of various buildings. The
plan was developed around architectural elements, dating from
the twelfth to the fifteenth century, from the cloisters of five
monasteries in France—Saint-Guilhem-le-Désert, Saint-Michel-
de-Cuxa, Bonnefont-en-Comminges, Trie, and Froville. As the
reconstructed cloister from the abbey of Saint-Michel-de-Cuxa
was to be the central and largest section of the museum, it
seemed appropriate to employ in the design of the tower of
The Cloisters some of the features of a tower still standing at
Cuxa, one of two which were formerly part of the abbey. The
Gothic Chapel, at the southwest end of the building, was modeled after thirteenth-century chapels at Carcassonne and Monsempron.

As the plans for The Cloisters progressed numerous other
Romanesque and Gothic architectural elements were acquired.
These, including the chapter house from Pontaut, the stonework from the choir of the church at Langon, some thirty
doorways and windows, and stained glass, have been incorporated functionally in the structure of the building. Although
decorative effects have often been obtained by arranging antique objects without relation to their original use, this proce-
dure was considered inconsistent with the purpose of a museum
and was avoided at The Cloisters. Reconditioning was likewise
avoided whenever possible; for though it is sometimes necessary to restore works of art which remain exposed to the elements, an inheritance from the past has often been irrevocably

destroyed by the attempt to bring old and new work into complete harmony.

Prominence has been given the exhibits by making the architectural setting unobtrusive. Though the backgrounds are mediaeval in style, the simplest precedents have been followed for the modern work. The modern capitals in the Romanesque Hall, for example, were based on unornamented prototypes so that they would not detract from the profusely carved Moutiers-Saint-Jean doorway or the Adoration group from Cerezo de Riotirón. Further, the figures of the Adoration group were placed in a niche over a doorway so that they might be seen at the proper height, but no attempt was made to copy their former setting.

The building materials have been kept subdued along with the architectural design. Millstone granite, quarried and cut by hand near New London, was in general used for the exterior of the building. Its warm tones recall stone found in southern France, and it is more durable and therefore more suitable for a large modern structure in New York than the stone which was commonly used for mediaeval buildings. In order to give the proper scale to the walls, the dimensions of the individual blocks were patterned after those of Romanesque buildings, in particular the church at Corneilla-de-Conflent, a few miles from Cuxa. To attempt to reproduce the rough rubble walls at Cuxa (probably covered over with plaster in the Middle Ages) would not have been feasible. For the interior stonework the principal material used was Doria limestone, quarried near Genoa in Italy. When sand-sawn and left without hand tooling it has the appearance of weathered stone and harmonizes well with the antique elements in the collection.

Color has been used sparingly for decoration, though we might have followed the precedent of Abbot Suger, who wrote of the building of the great abbey of Saint-Denis in the twelfth century: "We summoned skilled modelers and sculptors, who erected the central doors in which were sculptured statues which we caused to be gilded at great expense, . . . furthermore we caused the tower and the upper part of the gable to be ornamented in many colors. . . ." But it would not have been appropriate to provide a colorful setting for works of art which in the course of time have lost almost all vestiges of once resplendent polychromy.

Red roof and floor tiles, copied from examples excavated at Saint-Michel-de-Cuxa, have been used to give an effect like that of buildings in southern Europe; and here and there old materials, including beams for the ceilings, planks for the doors, and glass for the windows, help to create a suitable background for the exhibits. For the modern woodwork, window glass, and hardware simple designs have been followed, and inconspicuous modern lighting arrangements have been installed.

While it would be interesting to compare modern and mediaeval building methods and to describe in detail the preparation of various building materials, this subject must for the present be put aside. Examination of the exhibits in The Cloisters and comparison of old with modern work afford the best possible introduction to the study.

The site of The Cloisters, on ledges of rock commanding a view of the Hudson River, brings to mind the situations of mediaeval buildings at Mont-Saint-Michel, Basel, and Saint-Bertrand-de-Comminges. Rampart walls enclose a courtyard designed to be used as a parking space and to provide in connection with the building a convenient place from which to view the magnificent surrounding landscape. This courtyard and the entrance driveways are paved with Belgian blocks (taken from old New York streets) to suggest the cobblestones of old European towns.

The natural setting has been enhanced by extensive planting. Because of the severity of New York winters landscaping with the olive trees, fig trees, palms, and cypress typical of Mediterranean regions was out of the question, but the flowering crab-apple trees on the southern slope of The Cloisters property will recall the orchards and groves which often completely surrounded monasteries.

Within the walls of the building the landscaping is based on such mediaeval precedents as are available. The design of the gardens of the reconstructed cloisters from Cuxa, Trie, and Bonnefont presented a difficult problem, for no contemporary plans showing the layout of mediaeval gardens exist. Even the complete ninth-century plan of the monastery of Saint-Gall gives no clue to actual planting, except in the cemetery. In the Cuxa garden iris and other plants known in the Middle Ages have been used in a semiformal arrangement. Several apple trees were also planted there, as they were frequently grown in cloisters and some are still to be seen within the walls of the monastery of Saint-Michel-de-Cuxa. The walks were suggested by those of the central cloister in the plan of Saint-Gall. In the garden of the Trie Cloister yews, a cedar tree (instead of cypress), myrtle, ivy, and various flowers have been planted somewhat as in old cloisters still existent abroad.

Special attention has been given to the garden in the Bonnefont Cloister, which has been conceived of as a mediaeval garden of herbs and flowers (fig. 87). The plan has no particular prototype, but is based on mediaeval gardens as they are known to us in manuscript illuminations, tapestries, and paintings. Each variety of herb and flower has been labeled, so that visitors who wish to continue reading labels out of doors may identify them. Those growing in the Bonnefont Cloister are species mentioned in mediaeval texts and depicted in such works of art as the Unicorn tapestries (see figs. 72-77). Particularly useful was the list of herbs which Charlemagne gave directions to have grown in the imperial gardens. The list is preserved in *Capitulare de villis imperialibus,* issued in 812, and has often been reproduced. Gradually the Museum is collating various lists of mediaeval plants. A list of the plants grown in the Bonnefont Cloister garden in 1941, accompanied by a decorative plan, is available.

SUGGESTED ITINERARY. The octagonal Entrance Hall, above which rises the tower, is the starting point for a visit to the Museum.

The arrangement of the exhibition areas and terraces is shown in the accompanying plans. They may be visited in the following order: *main floor*—the Romanesque Hall, the Saint-Guilhem Cloister, the Romanesque Chapel, passageway to the West Terrace, the Chapter House from Pontaut, the Cuxa Cloister, the Nine Heroes Tapestry Room, the Early Gothic Hall, and stairway to the ground floor; *ground floor*—the

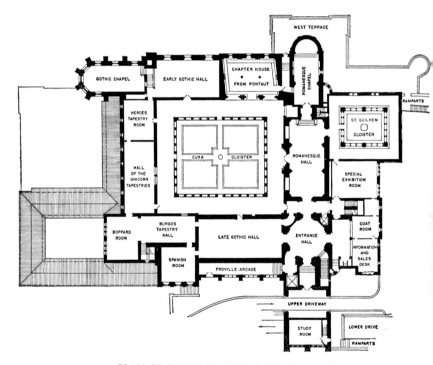

PLAN OF THE MAIN FLOOR OF THE CLOISTERS

Gothic Chapel, the Bonnefont Cloister, the Trie Cloister, the Fifteenth-Century Sculpture Hall, the Treasury, and stairway to the main floor; *main floor*—the Boppard Room, the Hall of the Unicorn Tapestries, the Burgos Tapestry Hall (by way of the Cuxa Cloister), the Spanish Room, the Late Gothic Hall, the Froville Arcade.

It is suggested that, at least on the first visit, the exhibits be seen in consecutive order, beginning with the Romanesque and continuing with those of the early and late Gothic periods.

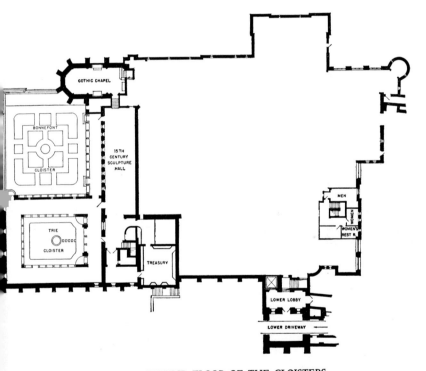

PLAN OF THE GROUND FLOOR OF THE CLOISTERS

# THE CLOISTERS

# THE ROMANESQUE HALL

THE ENTRANCE DOORWAY. More elaborate and more delicate in its ornament than the doorway from the chapel of the Knights Templars at Beaune, in the vestibule adjacent to the Entrance Hall, is the twelfth-century doorway from southwest France at the entrance to the Romanesque Hall. Although sturdy members and bold proportions were the fundamental considerations of the medieval architect, the fine-grained, soft white limestone of this doorway permitted the most intricate carving. Taking full advantage of the nature of their medium, the sculptors executed even the most minute details with consummate skill. The decorated voussoirs, keystone, and capitals with abacus blocks are effectively placed.

THE ARLANZA FRESCOES come from the chapter house of the monastery of San Pedro de Arlanza, which is south of Burgos, near Hortigüela. Tradition ascribes the founding of the monastery both to Wallia, the Visigothic king, and, with more probability, to the great Count of Castile, Fernán González, who bestowed favors on the monastery early in the tenth century. The church, now in ruins, was commenced in the eleventh century; building continued in the twelfth and thirteenth centuries, and parts were changed in the fifteenth and sixteenth centuries. On the basis of style the chapter house with its paintings may be ascribed to the early thirteenth century. Here a room, originally about 34 feet square and 12 feet high, was decorated from floor to ceiling with frescoes representing large and fantastic animals, framed with ornamental borders. In 1773 or 1774, or possibly somewhat earlier, the room was completely remodeled to permit the erection of a monumental staircase adjoining a large cloister (completed in

I

1617). Such of the frescoes as were not demolished were roughened with picks so that the new layer of plaster with which they were then covered would hold.

When Church and conventual property in Spain was sequestered in 1835-1837, the monastery at Arlanza became national property. In 1845 practically all the buildings were sold by national decree to a private citizen. When the roof of the chapter house collapsed and the plaster which for years had protected the walls began to crumble away, little by little the paintings were exposed to the elements. Fortunately the frescoes were removed to safety prior to 1929; otherwise at present very little would remain of a once noble series. They seem first to have been published in 1912.

The two principal sections of the Arlanza group were acquired for The Cloisters because they were thought to be among the best examples of decorative wall painting available;

FIG. I. A LION. FRESCO FROM SAN PEDRO DE ARLANZA
SPANISH, ABOUT 1220

2

and in fact they may well be considered the finest and most skillful of their kind in existence. In one section a lion is superbly depicted (fig. 1); below is a border of fish. In the other section is a dragon. The border beneath contains two confronted harpylike figures with human upper bodies on lower bodies of winged dragons, a fox and a goat dancing to the music produced by an ass playing on a harp, and two rabbits between two human figures.

The lion is closely paralleled by several lions in a Beatus manuscript in The Pierpont Morgan Library. In quality, in brilliance of design, and in dexterity of handling the frescoes do not suffer by comparison with the similar small-scale work of the manuscript illuminator. The manuscript, a commentary on the Apocalypse, was copied in the royal Cistercian convent of Las Huelgas, on the outskirts of Burgos, from the tenth-century codex formerly in San Salvador de Tavara (this is now thought to be in Madrid). The similarity of the manuscript and the frescoes and the proximity of their places of origin suggest the adoption of the date 1220 in the colophon of the manuscript as the date of the frescoes.

## THE ADORATION GROUP FROM CEREZO DE RIOTIRÓN.

The four sculptures composing the group from Cerezo de Riotirón, the Adoration of the Magi (figs. 2, 3), are from the same locality as the Arlanza frescoes and are almost contemporary with them. The showing of the works together affords opportunity for unusually interesting comparison, and in spite of the difference of medium certain conventions in rendering are used for both the animals and the figures. Very few well-preserved pieces of the size and quality of this group are to be seen in museums.

These sculptures, perhaps better than any others in The Cloisters, represent the monumentality of ecclesiastical sculp-

3

ture of the late Romanesque period. They bring to mind such imposing and developed creations as the portal sculptures of Saint-Gilles in southern France or those of Santiago de Compostela in Spain, which are their second cousins. In the style of the rhythmic drapery there is evidence of the same masterful handling as in the calligraphic lines of the Arlanza lion, which has been cited for "the extreme sophistication of the drawing." Although the drapery folds of the limestone figures are conventionalized, there is no monotony, owing to the variety in treatment.

The very mass of the stone block from which the Virgin and Child are hewn gives dignity to the scene. Joseph sits tranquilly at the Virgin's left side and adds the necessary balance to the two kings kneeling at her right. One of the kings, probably representing a historic personage who has not been identified, lifts his garment to bare what appears to be a deformed foot. Like the accessories—the book, the gifts, and Joseph's staff—the crowns were prominent in the composition.

Although three kings are usually represented in Adoration groups, sometimes fewer appear. As a photograph of this group in its original setting shows the composition to have been exactly as it is today, there is no reason for supposing that one of the kings has disappeared. The figures stood in a niche above an arch west of the south portal of the church. Groups of this kind were usually placed in tympana, but occasionally, especially in the Burgos region, where there are several similar groups, large figures are placed in settings that have no particular architectural significance.

The origin of this figure style is one of the most debated questions in mediaeval archaeology; for the present purpose it may best be said that sculpture of this kind appeared simultaneously in southern France and northern Spain towards the end of the eleventh century. By the end of the twelfth century

4

FIG. 2. THE ADORATION OF THE MAGI. SCULPTURE FROM THE CHURCH OF NUESTRA SEÑORA DE LA LLAMA, CEREZO DE RIOTIRÓN. SPANISH, ABOUT 1188

schools were more distinctly localized, and their particular characteristics can be more clearly pointed out.

The Adoration group from Cerezo is identical in style with other sculpture in the neighborhood of Burgos, notably the portal tympana of Moradillo de Sedano and Gredilla de Sedano, and the Adoration group and a large Virgin and Child at Butrera. The inscription IN ERA MCCXXVI (1188 by the modern, or Gregorian, calendar) on a capital on the façade of the church of Moradillo de Sedano provides evidence for an approximate date for the Adoration group from Cerezo.

THE REUGNY DOORWAY. The doorway from Reugny (fig. 4), at the entrance to the Saint-Guilhem Cloister, is in a style transitional from Romanesque to Gothic. Its construction may be compared with that of the Beaune doorway, with its massive tympanum, and with that of the entrance doorway (see p. 1), where the tympanum is omitted. In the Reugny doorway, however, the arches supported by the columns are pointed, and the tympanum is lobed and decorated. Originally two statues, perhaps of saints, were attached to the central columns, although only a small section of one figure has survived. The doorway was probably made at the end of the twelfth century.

The church at Reugny, except for the doorway, was a simple, barnlike building on the exterior. It was built of rubble and doubtless was originally covered with plaster. Nowadays, when stone is so easily cut by machine, designers of modern buildings in the mediaeval style would consider incongruous the use of so pretentious a doorway in conjunction with a simple structure.

THE TORSO OF CHRIST. The consummate skill of the mediaeval sculptor is attested by the twelfth-century

FIG. 3. JOSEPH, A FIGURE IN THE ADORATION
GROUP FROM CEREZO DE RIOTIRÓN

FIG. 4. DOORWAY FROM REUGNY
FRENCH, LATE XII CENTURY

painted wood torso of Christ from Lavaudieu, near Brioude. The graceful curves of the anatomical rendering and the flattened folds of the drapery are developed with great finesse. Appreciation of such a piece does not require the experienced eye of the connoisseur, and it is not necessary, as is so often the case in mediaeval sculpture, to discount provincial characteristics and exaggerations resulting from an effort to produce particular effects. Since cleaning, the true color values have been

8

FIGS. 5, 6. THE VIRGIN AND SAINT JOHN
PROBABLY ITALIAN, XIII CENTURY

revealed. The torso is painted flesh color, and the red and blue-green loin cloth (*perizonium*) is decorated with checks outlined in black. The head of this fine sculpture is now in the Louvre.

THE VIRGIN AND SAINT JOHN. In the wood statues of the Virgin and Saint John, placed at either side of the torso of Christ, the greater simplification in the rendering of the folds is in part accounted for by the fact that the figures

9

were made to imitate enameled metalwork (figs. 5, 6). The curls of the hair and the slight outlines denoting the eyes further show that the sculptor of these pieces was attempting, as did frequently the contemporary painter, to suggest metalwork. Although they were probably made in Italy in the thirteenth century, their technique recalls that used for Limoges and other enamels of the late twelfth and the early thirteenth century. It is not unlikely that an enameled reliquary decorated in relief with a Crucifixion group, including figures of the Virgin and Saint John, inspired these two sculptures.

The statues are carved in soft red pine. The surfaces are covered with a layer of gesso composed of fine gypsum and glue. For the modeling of the heads and some of the drapery folds, canvas was placed over a coarse plastic material. For the garments, the ground was overlaid with a very thin layer of tin foil, to reflect light through the colored oil glazes with which the tin foil was covered. Finally, both statues were coated with what appears to be a varnish of the ordinary spirit type.

The Virgin wears a golden yellow mantle ornamented in black patterns with occasional red spots. Her garment is red. Saint John's cloak is red, bordered with silver-gray geometric patterns. His tunic is yellow-brown with red and black decorations. The folds above the waist are drawn with calligraphic black lines; other shadows are indicated by black or green outlines. The faces are painted a light fawn color with very faint pink glazes for the cheeks. Saint John's hair is painted in a yellow-brown with conventionalized spiral curls in a dark red brown. The colors must be visualized not exactly as they appear today, but as considerably more brilliant and without crackle and blemishes.

THE LION FROM ZAMORA. The lion relief, in which Christ is symbolized as "the Lion of the tribe of Judah," was one of a pair set high up on either side of the gable of the portal of the church of San Leonardo at Zamora in Spain. This relief and its companion piece, with a lioness, were used, according to custom, as the guardians of the doorway of the church. The lion tramples on a serpent, a symbol of Satan; in the background are Christ crowning the Virgin, attended by the archangel Gabriel, and Saint Leonard of Aquitaine freeing two prisoners.

From several inscriptions on the portal, this relief may be dated about the middle of the thirteenth century. The considerable remains of color are unusual for stone sculpture and make comparison with the figures of the Adoration group opposite particularly interesting. It shows strikingly to what degree most mediaeval sculpture is now destitute of color and how important this final embellishment was in producing the desired effect.

THE MOUTIERS-SAINT-JEAN DOORWAY. The magnificent thirteenth-century Gothic doorway in the west wall of this gallery, originally at the entrance of the transept (?) of the once celebrated monastery of Moutiers-Saint-Jean, shows at its very best the unison of architecture and sculpture of the golden age of Gothic (fig. 7). Moldings, ornament, and figure sculpture, brilliantly carved, are harmoniously worked into a single unit. The large capitals above the outer columns once served to support the vaulting of the porch which, before its destruction, sheltered the doorway.

A story is told with the chisel; enlivened by the play of light and shade, carefully juxtaposed and balanced subjects are depicted. Each part bears a definite, integral relation to the whole, but particular attention is focused on the figures of King Clovis and his son King Clothar, which stand in canopied niches on either side of the doorway. According to tradition King Clovis, in the first year of his conversion to Christianity, probably 496, granted the monastery of Moutiers-Saint-Jean a charter of immunity, exempting it in perpetuity from all royal and ecclesiastical jurisdiction; in addition, he gave to the monastery as much land as could be encircled by a man riding on an ass in a single day. This donation was later confirmed by King Clothar.

In the Coronation scene in the center of the tympanum, the Virgin, who is treading on the tail of an adder, is crowned by Christ, who holds a flattened orb, or disk, which is carved as though studded with jewels. Christ, as prophesied in the Scriptures (Psalm 91.13), treads upon the lion and the adder, symbols of evil. Angels, probably Michael and Gabriel, bearing candlesticks, kneel at the sides. Above, on the voussoirs of the archivolt, are six adoring angels, the lower two probably carrying crowns (?), the middle two with chalices or candlesticks, the upper two swinging censers and carrying naviculae. The feathers on the angels' wings are indicated with paint, perhaps as decoration or perhaps as guide lines in the sections which the sculptor was yet to carve. The comparative simplicity of the moldings of the main arch contrasts with the elaborateness of the trefoil cusped arch, which is formed by grapevines that grow up the embrasures of the portal and frame the Coronation scene. The outer sides of the embrasures are flanked by columns in which are four seated figures in canopied niches. These figures represent the biblical forerunners of Christ. From left to right, in pairs, beginning at the bottom, they are: Elijah (?), with the raven above, and Melchizedek beside an altar, bearing a chalice (?); David (?), and Solomon holding the temple of Jerusalem; Abraham, with Isaac at his side, the angel and the ram on the left, and Moses with horns and the brazen serpent; and Saint John the Baptist with his long hair, and Simeon holding the Christ Child.

The monastery of Moutiers-Saint-Jean, at one time called

FIG. 7. DOORWAY FROM MOUTIERS-SAINT-JEAN
BURGUNDIAN, XIII CENTURY

Sanctus Johannes Reomaensis, is said to have been the earliest in Burgundy and appears to have been in existence before the time of Clovis. It was sacked in the years 1567, 1584,
and 1629 and almost completely destroyed during the French
Revolution. According to an eighteenth-century account, in
1567 a group of Huguenots entered the monastery by a ruse
and "broke the statues . . . of the Founder Princes, Clovis and
Clotaire." In 1900 these statues were in a garden at Moutiers-
Saint-Jean; subsequently they were in the collections of Michel
Manzi and others in Paris. Except for a small section which
served as a window, the doorway was walled up and left in a
deplorable condition until its removal in recent years.

The statues accord with their present setting in style of
carving, quality and color of stone, and measurements. Traces
of old red paint on the mantle of Clovis, which show that
these figures, like most mediaeval statues, were once polychromed, match similar traces on the doorway. The cor-
respondence, in size and location, of a square iron pintle in
the left-hand niche with parts of an iron fastening in the back
of the statue of Clovis proved conclusively the relation of this
figure to the niche.

A prosperous period of the abbey, under the protection of
the Dukes of Burgundy, began early in the thirteenth century
with important gifts of land and money. The monastery records reveal neither the gift of this doorway nor anything about
its makers. However, the period of most extensive building,
dating from 1257 to about 1285, when the monastery finally
fell badly into debt, coincides with the style of the doorway.
This style, which is inspired by similar architectural sculpture
on the cathedrals of Sens and Auxerre, is even more closely related to that of the doorway of the north transept of the church
of Notre-Dame at Semur-en-Auxois, the main portal of the
church of Notre-Dame at Cluny, the small tympanum from a

# THE MOUTIERS-SAINT-JEAN DOORWAY

former doorway of the north transept at the cathedral of Véze-
lay, and a tomb relief on the wall of the north side of the aisle
of the church of Saint-Père-sous-Vézelay. All are the work of
a single, homogeneous school of artists, who carried the great
cathedral style to these outlying communities. Whether they
also worked at the cathedrals or only studied the work of other
sculptors, remains a subject for research. At its best this work
was neither provincial nor local in its manifestations. In fact,
it often surpassed its prototypes in quality—possibly because
the artists working in more remote localities were free from the
feverish activity of the great centers.

# THE SAINT-GUILHEM CLOISTER

THE Saint-Guilhem cloister (fig. 8) has been planned around the unusual and magnificent series of capitals and other fragments from the upper cloister of the celebrated abbey of Saint-Guilhem-le-Désert. This Benedictine abbey was founded in 804 by Guilhem (William), Duke of Aquitaine, Count of Toulouse, and Prince of Orange, and until the twelfth century it was called Gellone after the once lonely valley in which it stood. Guilhem was one of Charlemagne's paladins and, according to some accounts, a close relative. The monk Witiza, better known as Saint Benedict, was a friend of Guilhem and had founded somewhat previously the neighboring monastery of Aniane. In 806, Guilhem retired to the abbey of Gellone and six years later died there in the odor of sanctity. The famous relic of the True Cross, given by the Patriarch of Jerusalem to Charlemagne in 800 and presented by him to Saint Guilhem, was one of the monastery's chief treasures.

The abbey became one of the most important in southern France. By the end of the eleventh century or perhaps early in the twelfth, an almost square, comparatively regular cloister was built south of the nave of the church. The great period of building, however, came in the twelfth century. The early cloister was flanked on the east by the south transept, the sacristy, and the chapter house, on the west by the refectory, and on the south by the infirmary and the apartments of the abbot. In 1165, the monastery, already one of the regular stops on the pilgrimage road from Toulouse to Compostela, was included among the seven minor pilgrimages imposed as penance upon the Albigensian heretics.

In an entry of the year 1206 the cartulary of the monastery refers to the "new cloisters," as distinguished from earlier

FIG. 8. ARCADES AND COURT OF THE SAINT-GUILHEM CLOISTER

entries mentioning "the cloister in front of the chapter house." This new cloister was no doubt the upper gallery, whence came most, if not all, of the Saint-Guilhem stonework now in the Museum.

In the wars of religion the monastery suffered at the hands of the Calvinists, who took possession of the place in 1568. During the French Revolution, the property was sold; first it was used for a cotton mill and then for a tannery. These undertakings were not successful, and finally the cloister was sold to a stonemason, who exploited it as a quarry for many years. Some of the sculptured parts of the cloister were gathered together in the church of Saint-Guilhem in the third quarter of the nineteenth century by the Abbé Léon Vinas, who further showed his interest in the monastery by writing what is still the best monograph on the subject. Most of the fragments, however, had been brought together by Pierre Yon Vernière, one-time justice of the peace at Aniane. He placed them as decorations in his garden and used many of the finest columns to support grape arbors. By 1906 these carvings had been brought to Paris, and later they were bought and sent to the United States by George Grey Barnard. He, perhaps better than anyone of his day, recognized in this material the best sculptural traditions.

The present architectural setting was suggested by the cloister of Saint-Trophime at Arles and those at Montmajour and Saint-Rémy. The high wall above the arcades around the court, like that at Arles, makes possible the use of a skylight which is not conspicuous from the walks. By this means the delicate material is protected from the elements and yet can be seen in natural light coming from the same direction as that in uncovered cloister courts.

The capitals (see fig. 9), many of them with the original limestone shafts and bases, others with somewhat later replace-

18

FIG. 9. A CAPITAL FROM SAINT-GUILHEM-LE-DÉSERT
FRENCH, BEFORE 1206

ments long associated with them, are in a style transitional from Romanesque to Gothic. It is difficult to relate the style of this elegant, unsurpassed mediaeval carving to sculpture elsewhere. Perhaps the long residence at Saint-Guilhem of unusually inspired and skilled artists and craftsmen vying with one another in an effort to make their work incomparably beautiful explains its sporadic appearance. In the dexterity and crispness of the cutting, in the freedom and perfection of the ornamentation, and, above all, in the composition of the areas which count for light and dark, this is supreme chisel work.

Local flora and fauna were used both naturalistically and conventionally in the decoration. Many of the capitals, chiefly those of the Corinthian type, are sheathed with curling acanthus leaves, rhythmically conventionalized. The beautiful basket-shaped capital in which the acanthus leaves sweep in bold spirals is a striking variation of the more customary form. One capital is closely patterned with flat, heart-shaped leaves of the black bryony vine. Another is covered with a lacework of vines, leaves, and tendrils. Outstanding among the historiated pieces is the "Hell" capital, representing sinners being led in chains to the mouth of Hell—a masterpiece of mediaeval sculpture. The Presentation of Christ in the Temple and the Massacre of the Innocents are depicted by other capitals.

The abaci also are freely ornamented with a profusion of vines and foliage motives into which are introduced fruits, birds, and exquisitely carved human and animal heads. For some of this ornamentation, classical forms were adapted with great spirit and individuality. A ribbon winding in angular folds across one abacus recalls a Greek fret pattern. In southern France classical ornament was revived long before the Italian Renaissance, having been suggested by the many surviving Roman monuments, particularly those in the region of the lower Rhône.

# THE SAINT-GUILHEM CLOISTER

Several of the column shafts are decorated. One is carved with broad acanthus leaves in low, flat relief; another seems to be a conventionalized rendering of the trunk of a palm tree; and a third is covered with an intricate chevron pattern. The cast-stone shafts are reproductions of the originals (see explanatory labels in the cloister). The pilaster decorated with acanthus spirals is perhaps the most memorable of the fragments. Even goldsmith's work is not more precise.

THE FOUNTAIN in the center of the cloister (see fig. 8) was once a capital in the church of Saint-Sauveur at Figeac. This capital was later made into a font, as was a companion piece still at Figeac. In style it is earlier than the Saint-Guilhem carvings; it has even been suggested that it may have been carved as early as the late eleventh century. As it was used to support heavy architectural members that were high above the floor, its boldly conceived, deeply cut ornamentation is more rugged than that of the delicate cloister capitals.

THE CORBELS AND WINDOWS. The ten humorous, grotesque corbels from the abbey of Notre-Dame-de-la-Grande-Sauve (la Sauve-Majeure) are used in the Saint-Guilhem cloister to support the ribs and cornice of the vaults over the cloister walks exactly as are similar ones at Montmajour. Originally these corbels, which are of the same period as the Saint-Guilhem carvings, were supporting members for an exterior cornice. The columns in the two windows overlooking the Hudson River probably also come from la Sauve, where they may have been used in the former cloister.

# THE ROMANESQUE CHAPEL

THE old stonework incorporated in the walls of the Romanesque Chapel (fig. 10) comes from the church of Notre-Dame-du Bourg at Langon. Gaufredus, at one time abbot of the monastery of Notre-Dame-de-la-Grande-Sauve, ordered this church to be founded as a dependency of the monastery in 1126, the year in which he became bishop of Bazas. The church must have been well under way before 1155, as it had received important gifts prior to this date. Raymond of Dax (Raimundus Aquensis), librarian of la Sauve, was in charge of the construction.

The town of Langon, which resisted such famous soldiers as Du Guesclin in 1374 and Montgoméry in 1566, was involved for many centuries in wars and rebellions; the church of Notre-Dame suffered accordingly. Of recent years all that remained was a portion of the choir, which had been divided into two stories by a wood floor. The lower part was used as a stable, and the upper rooms, which had been a club of the Jacobins during the French Revolution, were later a dance hall and a moving-picture theater.

Most of the important architectural remains which had been removed from the church at Langon were acquired by the Museum, together with a large section of the original choir wall. They have been brought together in the Romanesque Chapel and installed with comparatively little change in their functional arrangement. The missing parts of the choir have been reconstructed with simple architectural forms (see explanatory label in the chapel). The modern walls adjoining the first two large columns, which stood originally at the junction of the choir and the transept, are set back in order not to conceal such parts of the carving of the capitals as survived a

FIG. 10. THE ROMANESQUE CHAPEL

fourteenth-century remodeling of the transept. The cornice at Langon was 23 feet 6½ inches above the floor of the choir; in the present installation it is 17 feet. The width of the interior has been decreased proportionately from 23 feet 3 inches at Langon to 17 feet 3⅜ inches in the chapel. Thus the original elements are readily visible from the floor and predominate over the modern work.

FIG. 11. A CAPITAL FROM LANGON
FRENCH, XII CENTURY

The capitals from Langon do not appear to have a religious significance or any particular story to tell. The bending half-length figures recall Greek atlantes and caryatids in their cease-less effort to support the weight above them. Even the crowned heads which look away from the altar (fig. 11) cannot from the evidence obtained be verified as actual portraits, although they may possibly represent Henry II of England and his wife, Eleanor of Aquitaine, royal patrons who visited la Sauve in

1155. The various heads are beautifully carved with unusual emphasis on simple planes. In contrast to other sculptures of their period they are strikingly lifelike. The conventionalized leaf motives and the snail decorations of the abaci and cornice moldings are well suited to the vigorous, geometric carving.

No traces of original painted decoration have been found on the brownish white limestone of the church walls. The first of several coats of whitewash may have been applied soon after the building was completed.

The twelfth-century architecture of Notre-Dame-du-Bourg is not unlike that of other buildings in the region. Such motives as the snails are to be found in larger buildings, especially in the not distant cathedral of Bordeaux. But the sculptural decorations at Langon are not stylistically related to those of the other churches listed in a papal bull of the year 1246 as dependent on la Grande-Sauve.

In comparison with the delicate, almost jewel-like carving of the Saint-Guilhem architectural sculpture, this work may appear barbaric and unstudied. Small-scale, intimate sculpture usually failed in its decorative purpose when used for large buildings, but bold sculptural work was generally architecturally impressive. In the completeness of the ensemble and in the quality of the sculpture, no better example of twelfth-century architectural stonework could be acquired for The Cloisters. All the writers who have mentioned the remains are agreed as to their importance.

THE ALTAR. Besides the actual building with its decorations, various pieces of church furniture were essential to the established performance of the sacraments. Of these the altar, since the earliest times, has been the most important. In the larger churches there were often several. Some were made of gold and enriched with precious stones, some were painted or sculptured, and others were ornamented with enamel plaques. Often in Spain, particularly in the region of Lérida, raised and painted gesso work, simulating more costly materials, was applied to a wood foundation much as frosting is forced from a pastry bag.

The altar frontal incorporated in the modern altar in the Romanesque Chapel is one of the best surviving examples in that technique, although the colors have by this time lost much

of their original brilliance. The Virgin and Child are shown in the center of the panel, enthroned in a mandorla supported by four angels; eight apostles standing in arched niches complete the composition, which is framed by an inscription and borders with lions passant alternating with double palmettes. The inscription gives in Latin the names of six saints, Simon and Jude, Matthew and John, Thomas and Barnabas. The frontal came from the parish church of Ginestarre de Cardós. It is a pendant to one, dated 1225 (?), in the Barcelona Museum.

THE CIBORIUM. In the early Christian Church the ciborium was a canopy over the altar, supported on

FIG. 12. THE VIRGIN AND CHILD
BURGUNDIAN, XII CENTURY

26

columns. It is also known as a baldaquin, or baldacchino, from Baldacco, the Italian name for Bagdad, which exported to the West elaborate textiles used for altar canopies. From this tabernacle-like structure hung the receptacle that held the consecrated wafer. Soon the word ciborium was used to denote the container for this reserved sacrament.

The marble ciborium with gold and colored mosaic inlay decoration, now exhibited here, was until at least 1889 in the former church of Santo Stefano near Fiano Romano. The roofs, which are set in their original beveled grooves, are restorations that have the same dimensions and angles as those shown in a photograph of the ciborium when it was still standing at Santo Stefano in an apse of similar proportions to that of the Romanesque Chapel. Most of the existing ciboria of this type are still in Rome and the surrounding provinces. An almost identical edifice in the church of Sant' Andrea in Flumine near Ponzano was made about 1150 by the Roman marble workers Nicolaus Ranucius and his sons Giovanni and Guitonne.

THE VIRGIN AND CHILD. The Virgin enthroned was a theme which many a sculptor of the twelfth century was called upon to interpret. In its severe frontality and its exquisite stylization of form and drapery this Virgin enthroned has all the formality of an oft-repeated dogma and also the solemn dignity of a deeply-felt personal religious faith (fig. 12). The statue was carved from a single block of walnut, and was originally completely polychromed. The Virgin's gown and veil were green, bordered with vermilion, her hair was black and her eyes were inlaid with blue enameled glass (only one eyeball remains). This sculpture is related in style to the sculptures of the great portal (1120-1132) of the Cathedral of Saint-Lazare at Autun and may have come from a church of that town. It is one of the few surviving wood sculptures in the

27

round from that dynamic Romanesque school of Burgundy which sprang from the great abbey of Cluny. In its light, slender forms, in its sure design of drapery folds in ever-moving linear patterns, in its fresh interpretation of a well-loved theme our statue has all the vitality of Romanesque Burgundian art at its best.

THE CRUCIFIX. This crucifix of the twelfth century (fig. 13) is one of the most distinguished sculptures of its kind. To say that it is comparable to the finest mediaeval figures of Christ in Europe, such as the famous Courajod Christ in the Louvre, gives some idea of its importance. Only recently, after years of neglect, it was found in the church of the convent of Santa Clara in the Spanish province of León, near Palencia, where it hung behind an eighteenth-century altar in a horse-shoe-shaped niche at the east end of a chapel. An inscription in stone, placed above the crucifix, is said to have recorded its donation to the church in the year 1047; as this date is not consistent with the style of the piece, it is possible that the inscription was incorrectly deciphered and that the year should be read as 1147.

The crucifix is in an exceptionally fine state of preservation, except for three of the arms of the cross, which at some time were shortened (these have now been restored in order to obtain the original relation in scale between the figure and the cross). Even the iron fastenings holding the body to the cross are contemporary. It is likely that the ends of the crossbar were painted with figures of Mary and John, and that the Hand of God, the moon and the sun, or some other symbol was shown at the top. It is also probable that the letters INRI were painted either directly on the cross or on a separate panel placed above the head of Christ.

The figure of Christ and the cross retain most of their orig-

FIG. 13. CRUCIFIX. SPANISH, XII CENTURY

inal paint. The color scheme, like the carving, is simply but vigorously conceived. The flesh tints contrast with the black hair and beard, the gold diadem, which is studded with painted red and green jewels, and the once blue loincloth, bordered in gold. The effectiveness of the relation of certain planes to others has been achieved in part by the use of dark lines about three eighths of an inch wide. They serve to supplement the natural shadows and are further evidence of the desire to conventionalize. The cross is painted dark green with a gilded border studded with cabochonlike ornaments, blue, red, and green in repeated series. On the back of the cross much of the original paint still remains. In the center is the Lamb of God, and at the ends of the crossbar are portions of two of the four symbols of the Evangelists.

The figure of Christ is made of walnut and the cross of red pine. In places parchment is used over the wood to cover joints and to give a better surface on which to place the gesso. The entire surface of the crucifix is covered with gesso; in certain areas this is thick and has actually been modeled.

In Romanesque crucifixes the almost horizontal arms, the stylized, symmetrical anatomy, and the flattened, tubular folds of the drapery gave to the figures of Christ a rare spiritual composure. In the ensuing periods of unbridled emotionalism the treatment of devotional representations became painfully realistic. In this Spanish crucifix there are no contorted writhings, and emphasis on the gruesome details of the scene is avoided. Even the contrast between the crown, the symbol of Christ's regality, and the loincloth is not incongruous.

The literature describing Romanesque crucifixes and related sculptures is not only extensive but conflicting. On the one hand, it has long been believed by all but those intimately acquainted with the problem that the best pieces are French and that less good examples are apt to be Spanish. On the other hand, some scholars have made attempts to prove the contrary. The fine example in this chapel not only came from Spain but is demonstrably related to certain Spanish monuments of known provenance, including several in the Morgan collection of the Metropolitan Museum. One is a silver and silver-gilt processional cross from the church of San Salvador de Fuentes in the province of Oviedo. The figure of Christ on the crucifix is practically identical in its general aspects, as well as in all its important details, to a dated ivory figure of Christ on the interior of a famous reliquary made for Bishop Gonzalo Menendez (1162-1175), in the Cámara Santa of the cathedral of Oviedo.

FIG. 14
THE VIRGIN (?) AND A MONK
STAINED GLASS
FRENCH, XIII CENTURY

STAINED GLASS, in fact glass of all kinds, was much rarer in the Middle Ages than is generally realized. The windows of chapels and small churches may have been filled with transparent materials, such as parchment, but more usually they were open during the daytime and covered only when the shutters were closed at night. Ordinarily, when the windows of mediaeval buildings, except cathedrals and great churches, were glazed, almost clear, usually diamond-shaped quarries were used. Most twelfth-century glass has long since disappeared.

31

# THE ROMANESQUE CHAPEL

All the colored glass now in the Romanesque Chapel dates from the thirteenth century. The two windows in the apse, at either side of the central window with grisaille, are composed of brilliantly colored panels believed to have come from a church in Troyes. They represent Christ (?) with an apostle (?), the Virgin (?) and a monk (fig. 14), a bishop receiving a kneeling man, and a group of figures from an Adoration scene. This glass is of the type and quality of windows at Chartres and Bourges.

THE DOORS. The massive, iron-bound, planked doors at the entrance to the chapel are unusual both in size and in preservation. Such doors protected a church and its treasures from marauders and withstood all but the heaviest battering rams. As twelfth- and thirteenth-century doors usually received hard wear, they were replaced from time to time, a fact which in part accounts for the relatively small number of examples still in existence in Europe.

# CHAPTER HOUSE FROM PONTAUT

NO architectural unit could be more perfectly suited to The Cloisters than the twelfth-century chapter house (figs. 15, 16) from the former abbey of Notre-Dame-de-Pontaut. In both style and period, as well as in size, this room is well adapted to the adjacent Cuxa Cloister. The chapter house is a complete architectural ensemble in the Romanesque style and a fitting supplement to the other important documents of mediaeval art in the collection. Stone for stone and brick for brick the room was carefully taken down and re-erected here. Only the floors and plaster vaults are restorations.

In every abbey the most important part, after the church, was the chapter house, in which the monks assembled each morning for discussion of the business of the convent. Sometimes an ordinary room was the meeting place of the chapter, but often, particularly in the late Middle Ages in England, a separate building was erected for this purpose. The monks sat on benches around the walls. The abbot usually had a separate or a raised seat at the back of the room. At Pontaut his seat may have been placed where a doorway (now filled in) was cut through the back wall when the room was used for a stable.

The few structures of this kind remaining in France, for instance those at Saint-Georges-de-Boscherville and Fontenay, were very similar to the Pontaut room: they usually opened on the cloister walk with three large arches and were adjacent to the church of the monastery. At Pontaut the room was separated from the south transept of the church by the sacristy and the armarium (library closet). The door originally leading to the sacristy has been walled up, and a new door leading from the Romanesque Chapel has been added. The dormitory was above the chapter room, as in most monasteries.

The abbey of Notre-Dame-de-Pontaut (also called Pontault, Ponteau, and Pons Altus) was founded by Geraldus, abbot of Dalon, about 1115. It was at first an abbey of the Benedictine order, but later, in 1151, in the time of Gaufredus—who had become its first abbot about 1125—the monastery was given to the Cistercians and placed under the rule of Pontigny. It was connected also with the abbey of Jouy, which was founded and favored by the kings of Navarre.

As yet the archives of the monastery have not been located; but the style of the existing chapter house, armarium, sacristy, and the remains of some of the adjoining buildings suggest a dating in the middle of the twelfth century for the early architecture. It is likely that the chapter house was built prior to the year 1151, for after the *Apologia ad Guilelmum* of Saint Bernard (about 1127) the Cistercians tried to banish all sculpture from their churches and other buildings and thereafter had to depend for effect on purely architectural forms. The Romanesque Hall in The Cloisters, with its simple capitals and moldings, is reminiscent of the sturdy, severe Cistercian work found at Pontigny and related monasteries. Since the cloister at Pontaut, a portion of which has been reconstructed at The Toledo Museum of Art, was not built until the fifteenth century, it offers no clue to the dating of the chapter house.

The abbey was partly destroyed by the Huguenots in 1569; by 1572 only a priest, seven monks, and a wounded soldier were in residence there. In 1791, during the French Revolution, the buildings were sold to Dyzez de Samadet. His only daughter married a member of the Poudenx family, who was related to the last abbot of Pontaut, and his brother was a deputy at the Convention and later a senator of the Empire. Peasants now occupy the dilapidated structures that formerly belonged to one of the thriving monasteries of Europe, and the place is rarely marked on any but the most detailed maps of the region.

34

FIG. 15. THE CHAPTER HOUSE FROM NOTRE-DAME-DE-PONTAUT
FRENCH, XII CENTURY

FIG. 16. THE INTERIOR OF THE CHAPTER HOUSE
FROM PONTAUT

The shape of the interior of the chapter house is irregular,
the corners not forming true right angles. The walls are not
quite parallel. The room measures 37 feet 8 inches along the
cloister, only 2 inches more on the opposite wall, and 25 feet 4
inches on the sides. The two central columns supporting the
round-arched ribs of the vaults divide the ceiling into three
bays. The west wall is pierced by three windows, which were
never glazed; there are hinges for shutters and holes for iron

bars. The carvings, moldings, and construction provide a lesson in mediaeval stonework. The varied decorations of the capitals (see fig. 17), the abaci, and the keystone bosses of the vaults include stars, rosettes, palmettes and other leaf forms, interlaced basket patterns, and confronted birds picking at grapes, pine cones, and an unidentified fruit. On the exterior the capitals are somewhat simpler in design.

In one wall and in some of the wall ribs brick supplements the soft, yellow limestone. The style of the brickwork is consistent with that used elsewhere at Pontaut and recalls similar work—for instance, that at Tournus, where brick was used even more extensively in combination with even less stone. The stone is thought to have been obtained at Dumes, beyond Hagetmau; probably because the builders had ex-

FIG. 17. A CAPITAL
FROM PONTAUT

hausted their supply of this material, locally baked bricks were used to complete the room. The bricks of the wall are approximately 15 inches wide, 2¾ inches high, and 10 inches deep.

Originally the walls were plastered, perhaps frescoed, and the ribs, as can be seen from traces of color here and there, were also painted. In the present installation it has seemed preferable not to attempt restoration of the stones and not to fill the joints completely. As the original floor tiles were missing when the room was acquired for The Cloisters, a twelfth-century tile from the church at Cuxa was used as a model for the tiles manufactured for the present flooring; this has been inserted in the floor near the southwest window.

37

# THE CUXA CLOISTER

ALL the capitals of this cloister; nineteen abaci, of which only two are ornamented; twenty-five bases; twelve shafts; seven arches; and part of the parapet coping are from the former twelfth-century cloister of the famous abbey of Saint-Michel-de-Cuxa (see frontispiece and fig. 18; see also explanatory labels in the cloister). This monastery was founded in 878 by the monks from the Benedictine monastery at Saint-André-d'Exalada, which had been destroyed in the previous year by an avalanche. At the suggestion of the emperor Charles the Bald, the abbot of Cuxa placed his "fifty monks and twenty servants, his already numerous lands, the thirty volumes of his library, and his five hundred sheep, fifty mares, forty pigs, two horses, five donkeys, twenty oxen, and one hundred other large animals with horns" under the protection of Count Miron, the founder of the line of counts of Conflent and Cerdagne. Under this auspicious patronage the monastery buildings were finished in 883. The first church was replaced by a considerably larger edifice, begun in 955 and consecrated in the presence of seven bishops in 974. The church and the monastery were dedicated to the archangel Michael, the favorite saint of a great patron of Cuxa, Count Séniofred of Cerdagne, as well as to the titular saint of the earlier church, Saint Germain, bishop of Auxerre. Wood from the Holy Manger was notable among the many gifts to the abbey, which was referred to as *monasterium proesepii Domini.*

The abbey attained great renown. In the last quarter of the tenth century there came to it such famous personages as Saint Peter Urseolus (Doge Pietro Orseolo of Venice), who joined the community as a novice, and two hermits, Marinus and Saint Romuald (Romualdo, the founder of the Camaldolese

FIG. 18. PART OF THE EAST ARCADE OF THE CUXA CLOISTER

order). Oliva, abbot of Cuxa from 1008 until 1046, was in his day the most celebrated personality in southern France and northern Spain. Soon after his election at Cuxa he received the additional offices of abbot of Santa María de Ripoll and bishop of Vich. He was distinguished as a writer and a poet and is accredited with having built the cathedral of Vich and the abbey church at Ripoll. His chief architectural contributions at Cuxa included the restoration of the old Mozarabic church and the construction of the ciborium described by the monk Garcia (see p. 44) and the church in which the fragments of the manger were preserved.

The records of the monastery during the succeeding centuries are interesting but not unusual. Arnald, abbot from 1188 until 1203, managed the affairs of the abbey so badly that he was deposed by order of Pope Innocent III.

The cloister at Cuxa was in all probability built in the second half of the twelfth century, before the time of the shiftless Arnald, as it is unlikely that extensive building operations were carried on under an abbot who alienated property belonging to his monastery. The closely related cloister capitals at Saint-Martin-du-Canigou and at Serrabona might offer a suggestion for the dating of those at Cuxa but for the fact that neither group can be definitely dated on documentary evidence, although the church of Serrabona is known to have been consecrated in 1151. The stylistically comparable capitals on the south side of the cloister at Elne are believed to have been executed when Guillem Jordà was bishop (1172-1186), for he was the first prelate to be buried in the cloister. A similar date for the Cuxa capitals is confirmed by the related capitals in the cloister of Santa María de Ripoll, which were carved in the last third of the twelfth century.

The sacking of the monastery of Cuxa in 1654 by the troops of a local count, who had ordered that the fortifications be torn down, was only the beginning of long years of despair for generation upon generation of monks. In 1793, three years after the decree of the "Civil Constitution of the Clergy," the French Revolution brought ruthless plundering and pillaging, and finally the monastery was sold in parts to three inhabitants of the region. At this time ten arcades from the cloister were removed to a bathing establishment at Prades. Most of the rest of the stonework was dispersed over the countryside. The arcades from Prades, together with other scattered elements, are now being reassembled at Cuxa, but the major portion of the capitals and many other carved elements from Cuxa are at The Cloisters. A twelfth-century marble fountain from the center of the cloister is at Eze-Village on the Riviera, in the possession of Mme Jacques Balsan; two capitals are in the Louvre, one is in the Museum of Fine Arts, Boston, and a fourth in the Pitcairn collection at Bryn Athyn, Pennsylvania. The fountain in the cloister of the Pennsylvania Museum of Art, Philadelphia, is also said to be from Cuxa.

The antique portions of the New York reconstruction of the Cuxa cloister, beginning at the northeast corner, have been kept together wherever possible. When additional stone was necessary to supplement the original elements, Languedoc marble was obtained from the massive mountain which lies between Ria and Villefranche, where the stone for Cuxa was cut in the twelfth century. These quarries in the neighborhood of Cuxa have for centuries supplied the local builders with this most unusual mottled light red and gray-white stone. They also furnished the polished marble used for the decoration of the Grand Trianon at Versailles and the mammoth columns of the Arc du Carrousel in Paris.

At present excavations are in progress at Cuxa, and no doubt more information about the monastery buildings will soon be forthcoming. The results will be of great interest, inasmuch as a recently discovered plan, dated 1779, is at variance with the usually accepted measurements for the original cloister. It has been described as rectangular, the walks at right angles to the church being 156 feet 2 inches long, those parallel to the church, 128 feet 7 inches. The cloister as now reconstructed is only a little more than half its original size (89 feet by 78 feet 4 inches), and the width of the walks has been decreased accordingly from 15 feet to 12 feet. On the long sides of the original cloister the eighteen columns between the corner piers were divided into groups of six by two intermediate piers; these have been omitted in the present arrangement.

The reconstruction was based on studies of the original site and on the evidence offered by original fragments, as well as on notes and drawings, some of which were made in the nineteenth century by E. Viollet-le-Duc and J. Taylor, who saw the cloister before it was completely demolished. The floor tiles were patterned after old ones specially excavated from the former walks at Cuxa. The timber roof, resting on stone corbels, and the roof tiles were suggested by precedents found at Cuxa and elsewhere. In this connection it is interesting to note that in Mediterranean regions the process of manufacturing tiles has varied little since mediaeval times; the clays used and the shapes are the same, and the baking processes are similar.

The Cuxa capitals (see figs. 19-22) are vigorously carved with monumental, architectonic feeling. The planes are simple and clearly defined with characteristic Romanesque vitality, creating a play of light and shadow. The figures consist of human and animal forms, rudely executed with little emphasis on realistic representation. Some of the capitals are fashioned in the simplest block forms; they serve as solid and adequate transitions between the column shaft and the abacus. Others are suggested by capitals of the traditional Corinthian and composite types but are ornamented with a repertory of their

FIG. 19

FIG. 20

FIG. 21

FIG. 22

CAPITALS FROM SAINT-MICHEL-DE-CUXA. FRENCH
SECOND HALF OF THE XII CENTURY

own. The human heads and figures, the lions, apes, birds, acanthus leaves, and other conventionalized motives—palm trees, palmettes and half palmettes, vines, bunches of grapes, and rosettes—are fascinatingly combined. As these capitals do not appear from the decorations to have been conceived for use in any particular sequence, they have been arranged according to type, beginning with the simpler, possibly earlier, forms and continuing with the more sophisticated examples.

The pairs of confronted birds and animals must have been inspired, at least indirectly, by textiles and other objects of art brought from the Near East. Certain of the capitals may relate naïve episodes taken from bestiaries or classical stories reminiscent of the fables attributed to Aesop. For others one is tempted to supply didactic meanings and even perhaps to recognize Daniel in the lions' den and other heroes. But it is difficult, if not impossible, to identify the representations which appear in these unrelated scenes.

CAPITALS FROM THE CIBORIUM. A more strictly classical type of capital was produced at Cuxa a century earlier. The two large white marble capitals here, together with a third still near the monastery of Saint-Michel-de-Cuxa, are no doubt from the ciborium constructed in the monastery church by the abbot Oliva about 1040 (see p. 40). In this year the ciborium was described in great detail in a letter written by the monk Garcia. This account says it was composed of four pink marble shafts 7 feet high, each bearing a white marble capital of the Corinthian type.

THE FRÍAS DOORWAY. A nineteenth-century account of the church of San Vicente Mártir at Frías describes in considerable detail the main portal, which was presumably made early in the thirteenth century at the order of Alfonso VIII,

King of Castile (1158-1214), who instigated various reconstruction projects at the church. A great fire swept the church
in the sixteenth century, and when the tower fell in 1879 the
portal was destroyed.

Eighty stones from this portal, gathered together at the
church, are incorporated in the reconstruction of the doorway
in the north wall of the cloister. A group of particularly well-
carved pieces was at one time on exhibition at the main building of the Museum. The problem of arranging these miscel-
laneous stone carvings as they would have been in the Middle
Ages was doubly difficult owing to the fact that a number of
stones had been used in an earlier construction and then had
been reworked and used again. At the sides of the present installation two openings have been made so that the backs of
some of these reworked stones can be seen.

The reconstruction is based upon a study of the individual
stones and related monuments in Spain. The ornamental carving is crisply cut and effective. The various voussoir blocks are
like illustrations for a picture book, except that they are placed
on a doorway, and those which are high up can scarcely be
read. Some of the individual stones may be identified as follows: *second arch* (beginning with the eighth stone from the
right), a monk blessing a man starting on a journey; the monk
wounded; the monk's deathbed; a wild rose; a woman, possibly
symbolizing Victory or Courage, between two fighting warriors; a figure symbolizing Lust; (on the last stone) two demons
dragging a miser to hell; *third arch* (beginning at the right),
the Visitation and a seated male figure, possibly Joachim; the
Flight into Egypt; the devil tempting Christ to turn stones into
bread; Christ raising Jairus's daughter; Christ sending forth
the disciples to preach (?); Christ healing a dumb man; the
Entry into Jerusalem (on two stones); Christ washing the feet
of the disciples; the Last Supper (on two stones); the Betrayal.

45

THE NARBONNE ARCH. The white marble arch over the doorway near the wall fountain is said to have come from the former church of Saint-Cosmus at Narbonne; an arch identical in style is now at the church of Saint-Paul-Serge at Narbonne. This work is less provincial than the similar Cuxa carving of the same period. The grotesque animals—mantichora, pelican, basilisk, harpy, griffin, asp, centaur, and lion—and the acanthus molding are fashioned with great vigor.

FOUNTAINS AND LAVABO. The central fountain (see frontispiece), possibly a font made into a fountain, comes from Saint-Genis-des-Fontaines, and the wall fountain in a recess at the northeast corner of the cloister wall, except for the two blocks supporting the basin, is from the monastery of Notre-Dame-du-Vilar. Although neither fountain came from Cuxa, their style is contemporary with that of the capitals and the pink marble came from the same quarries. The stone slab placed above the basin of the wall fountain and the basin itself were not used together when these two elements were found at Vilar, and an old photograph shows that the slab was at one time used as the tympanum of a doorway. But an examination of both elements, the two holes through which the water flowed, and parts of the doorway confirms the opinion that the slab and the basin formerly composed a fountain as they do now. The basin may have served as a reservoir from which buckets were filled or as a lavabo where the monks could wash their hands. Lavaboes such as the thirteenth-century Burgundian example in the southwest corner of the cloister had two basins, one for the washing of hands and the other for the eucharistic vessels, which could be placed on the shelf above.

NOTE. The statue of Saint James the Greater at the entrance to the Nine Heroes Tapestry Room is discussed on page 90.

# THE NINE HEROES
# TAPESTRY ROOM

THE only sets of fourteenth-century tapestries of which substantial portions have survived are the Apocalypse tapestries at Angers and the Nine Heroes tapestries at The Cloisters (figs. 23-26). Few other pieces of the period exist.

The Cloisters set originally consisted of three tapestries, each more than twenty-one feet wide and about sixteen feet high and each representing three heroes, life size in scale, surrounded by smaller figures in an architectural setting. This set, like the Apocalypse, had been cut up and dispersed in the course of time. Nevertheless it has been possible for The Cloisters over a period of twenty years to assemble from four different owners ninety-five fragments of various sizes which have now been pieced together to form more than two thirds of the original set. Five of the nine heroes and almost all of the accompanying smaller figures have been recovered.

Ninety-one of the ninety-five fragments were bought by Baron Arthur Schickler just after the Franco-Prussian War for his castle at Martinvast, five miles from Cherbourg, and made into window curtains. Among these were three cardinals that belonged with a large fragment, the King Arthur, which the Metropolitan Museum has owned since 1932. Two figures sewn to the left side of the Arthur at least as early as 1877, when these fragments were in the Chabrières-Arlès collection in Lyons, have now been properly placed at the right of the tapestry of the Hebrew heroes. Another small figure in this tapestry had passed through many hands. Still another piece, the most recently acquired fragment, came from a castle in Ireland, where it had once come from Paris by way of London.

The most complete tapestry represents two Hebrew heroes with courtiers and warriors. The heroes are seated on Gothic thrones in elaborate Gothic niches; both are bearded and both are crowned. The figures are presented in contemporary mediaeval dress, with utter disregard for historical accuracy; even Joshua wears a crown. He is identified by the dragon on his shield and a "sun in its glory" on the drapery at his feet. King David, with a golden harp, is in the center, and Judas Maccabeus would have occupied the place in the tapestry where a doorway now leads to the Cuxa Cloister. The little figures— spearmen and archers, courtiers and musicians—enliven the composition. A lady plays a rebec, another a harp, and another a psaltery; one holds a cheetah, another a falcon, still another a tiny dog.

On the wall opposite, separated by a window with a fourteenth-century stained-glass panel, are the pagan heroes, Alexander the Great or Hector with a lion in a chair emblazoned on his shield and Julius Caesar with a double-headed imperial eagle in sable on gold. Only the central figure is missing.

But of the three Christian heroes only the King Arthur has been found; Charlemagne and Godfrey of Bouillon have disappeared. Arthur is clearly identified by the three crowns, representing England, Scotland, and Brittany, on his surcoat and on his banner.

The theme of the Nine Heroes—called in mediaeval English the Nine Worthies and in French *les Neuf Preux*—was developed and made popular about 1310 by a jongleur named Jacques de Longuyon in his "Vows of the Peacock" (*Les Voeux du paon*). There were numerous representations of the Nine Heroes and their counterparts, the Nine Heroines, in fourteenth-century sculpture, painting, manuscripts, and goldsmith's work, and many a great nobleman of the time owned sets of tapestries illustrating these subjects.

48

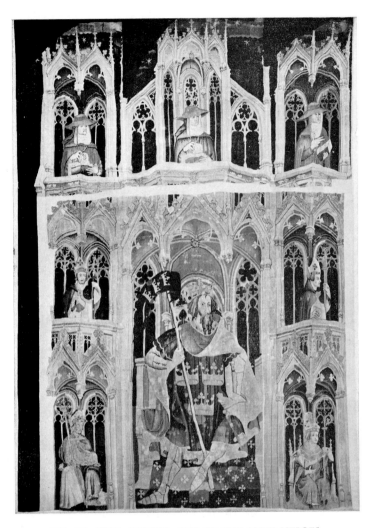

FIG. 23. KING ARTHUR. ONE OF THE NINE HEROES
ORIGINALLY PART OF A TAPESTRY WITH THREE CHRISTIAN HEROES
FRENCH, LATE XIV CENTURY. WORKSHOPS OF NICOLAS BATAILLE

FIG. 24. COURTIERS AND BANNERS WITH THE DUKE OF BERRY'S
ARMS. DETAIL FROM THE TAPESTRY OF THE HEBREW HEROES

A recurrent detail in the Heroes tapestries at The Cloisters furnishes a clue to the identity of the original owner of the set. Ten of the fourteen banners flying from turrets in the Hebrew Heroes tapestry (see fig. 24) and the escutcheons in the vaults above David and Joshua display the golden fleurs-de-lis of France on an azure ground within an indented border of red. Since these are the arms of Jean, Duke of Berry, third son of King Jean of France, it may be supposed that the set was made to Berry's order or woven for him as a gift.

With the exception of a set of Heroes tapestries woven with gold and silver threads, no similar tapestries are recorded in the inventories and account books of the duke. However, a series of Heroines, probably the companion set to The Cloisters Nine Heroes, is listed and described in an inventory of the possessions of Berry's nephew, Charles VI, made shortly before his death in 1422. The presence of the Berry arms on

50

Charles's set suggests that these Heroines also belonged to Berry.

The Apocalypse tapestries are the only woven pictures surviving that afford a suitable basis for comparison with the Heroes tapestries. During the loan exhibition of French tapestries held at the Metropolitan Museum in 1947-1948, pieces from both sets were examined side by side. Both series are woven with double weft threads and with approximately twelve and a half ribs, or warp threads, to the inch. The same restricted colors, with similar shading in the same light and dark tones, appear in both sets. Shaded reds and blues predominate, recurring at intervals in the pattern. In both sets the stonework, woven in a golden tan color slightly more faded in some places than in others, is silhouetted against a very dark blue, almost black sky. The five heroes, like the large Angers figures, are seated under vaulted architectural structures, and such details as the butterflies and the foliage at the outer edges of the tapestries are comparable. If the Heroes tapestries were not woven in the same workshops as the Angers Apocalypse, they must have been produced under virtually identical supervision and by similarly trained weavers.

We know that most of the Angers Apocalypse tapestries were woven before 1384 for the Duke of Berry's brother, Louis, Duke of Anjou, by Nicolas Bataille, master tapestry-weaver and merchant of Paris (died about 1400). And we know that Berry also ordered textiles from Bataille. Payments to Bataille as early as 1374 are recorded in the voluminous but incomplete account books kept by Berry's treasurers, although the entries do not describe or itemize the purchases, merely noting their cost. The fact that Bataille's widow is listed among the creditors claiming settlements from the duke's estate in 1416 indicates that further orders were received from him.

The Heroes tapestries may have been made for the Duke

of Berry's palace at Bourges and may actually have been woven there. This possibility is suggested by an extract from a contemporary document which can no longer be found in the Bibliothèque Nationale but which was noted by A. de Champeaux and P. Gauchery in their *Travaux d'art exécutés pour Jean de France, Duc de Berry* (Paris, 1894). According to this record there was a "payment made in 1385 to Jehan le Prestre, roofer and plasterer, for having completely reroofed the great hall of the palace at Bourges, where formerly the grain received as tithes by the duke had been kept and where *they were now making his tapestry* at the same time that they were cutting stones for the palace."

The duke had statues of the Nine Heroes placed in gabled niches above one of the great mantelpieces of his palace at Bourges. An exterior wall with turrets and balustrades, still standing among the remains of this fourteenth-century castle, may well have inspired the framework of one of The Cloisters tapestries. High up on several of the remaining interior walls there are friezes with leaf motives which are similar to the schematic frieze that divides the upper and lower sections of the Heroes tapestries. Little turrets with open windows like those in the tapestries appear again and again in the Bourges stonework; for instance, the breast of one of the mantelpieces is divided by five such structures.

In the stained-glass panels formerly in the Sainte Chapelle of the duke's palace at Bourges there are elements that show, in both the design and the coloring, a relationship with the tapestries. The placing of large figures in niches and the silhouetting of some of the figures against Italian brocades are common to both. The architectural structures with groined vaults, the thin columnar sections supporting gables ornamented with crockets and finials, and the quatrefoil tracery below some of the figures are very similar. The tonality of the

FIG. 25. ALEXANDER THE GREAT (?). ONE OF THE NINE HEROES
ORIGINALLY AT THE LEFT OF THE PAGAN HEROES TAPESTRY
FRENCH, LATE XIV CENTURY. WORKSHOPS OF NICOLAS BATAILLE

faces and hair is remarkably close. But even more striking is the similar use of yellow, outlined in red, for the crockets and finials of the architecture.

The stained glass and the stylistically related statues of prophets and apostles from the Sainte Chapelle are generally believed to have been influenced if not actually designed by André Beauneveu (died before 1403), the general superintendent of Berry's artistic enterprises, in the last quarter of the fourteenth century. There is, however, no more than a general resemblance in composition and in style between the heroes in the tapestries and the seated figures in the only paintings unquestionably accepted by modern scholars as the work of Beauneveu, twenty-four miniatures painted in the thirteen-eighties for the Duke of Berry's Psalter (B.N. ms. fr. 13091).

Among the manuscript paintings which seem closer in some respects to the Heroes tapestries are those in the Albumasar astrological treatises in the Pierpont Morgan Library (M. 785). These not only show seated figures comparable to the heroes but also have certain details, in particular the wind-swept veils, which have definite affinities to the drawing in the tapestries. This manuscript, presented on June 7, 1403, to the Duke of Berry, was "created" by Abbot Lubertus, who from 1394 until 1417 directed a center for the illumination of manuscripts in the abbey of St. Bartholomew of Eechoutte, near Bruges.

The attribution of manuscript illuminations of this period to specific artists is difficult. The attribution of tapestries on the basis of their relation to manuscript paintings is even more difficult, for comparison is complicated by our inability to know what latitude a master weaver and his fellow craftsmen had in interpreting the cartoons supplied by a designer. And it has not been possible to single out as the designer of the Nine Heroes tapestries any of the masters who worked for the Duke of Berry in the last decades of the fourteenth century.

54

FIG. 26. JULIUS CAESAR. ONE OF THE NINE HEROES
ORIGINALLY AT THE RIGHT OF THE PAGAN HEROES TAPESTRY
FRENCH, LATE XIV CENTURY. WORKSHOPS OF BATAILLE

# THE EARLY GOTHIC HALL

EARLY Gothic sculpture, like the Romanesque, was largely the handmaid of architecture. On the exterior, cathedrals and churches had portals and porches enriched with statues. On the interior, statues were placed on piers and in niches and as adornments on church furniture. The freestanding figure, dissociated from the architectural niche, was uncommon.

By the fourteenth century every community had its cathedral, church, or chapel, and artists were able to devote their energies to sculpture and other arts which were not necessarily a part of architecture.

STATUES OF THE VIRGIN AND CHILD. The favorite theme of the Gothic sculptor, the Virgin and Child, is represented in this gallery by a number of statues. These show the variations in treatment characteristic of different schools of Gothic sculpture, together with certain traditional features that were common to all.

The Virgin from the thirteenth-century choir screen of Strasbourg Cathedral, one of the great monuments of the Middle Ages, is perhaps the most important Gothic sculpture on this side of the Atlantic (fig. 27). This Queen of Heaven is as regal as any we find in art. With majestic but simple grace she expresses the most ennobling qualities of the Gothic period. The angular Gothic folds of the gilded mantle with rich borders studded with red and green jewels contrast with the simplicity of the Virgin's gown. Below the carefully modeled neck the severe white border of the undergarment provides a strong accent. The modeling of the gentle features—wide brow, almond-shaped eyes, delicate mouth, and pointed chin—is enlivened by the painting of the flesh and such details as the

FIG. 27. THE VIRGIN FROM THE CHOIR SCREEN
OF STRASBOURG CATHEDRAL. RHENISH,
1247-1252

eyeballs and the arched eyebrows. The old paint covering this sandstone sculpture was miraculously preserved under coats of later repaint.

As a result of the relocation of the altar required by changes in ritual introduced in the time of Louis XIV, the choir screen of Strasbourg Cathedral was demolished in 1680. Its design, however, is preserved in a drawing of about 1660. Here the Virgin is depicted as the fourth in a series of eight figures, mostly apostles, adorning the upper part of the façade of the screen. Two angels support the Virgin's veil, and two others are flying above. The Child does not sit on his mother's arm, but is seated on a rosebush and offers to his mother what appears to be a fruit on which a bird is perched. A comparison of the measurements, stylistic analogies, and various details of this work with the other existing choir-screen statues has made it possible to identify The Cloisters Virgin as the missing Virgin from Strasbourg. As the choir screen can be dated between 1247 and 1250 or at all events before 1252 when it was recorded as in place, it may be assumed that the sculpture was completed by this time. For three decades after its sale at public auction in London in 1913, for the sum of eighty-nine pounds and five shillings, the Strasbourg Virgin was in a private collection near Paris.

The imposing fourteenth-century Virgin and Child from the Paris region—which also retains its complement of original polychromy—should be compared to the very similar but badly mutilated and weathered limestone sculpture to the right. The importance of painting and gilding in mediaeval sculpture is strikingly shown in the more complete statue. In this figure the gentility, the dignity, and the repose of the Virgin are portrayed with mastery (fig. 28). Her composure is expressed by the relaxed stance, the graceful swing of the figure forming an S-curve. Most other Gothic representations of the subject suffer

FIG. 28. THE VIRGIN AND CHILD
FRENCH (ÎLE-DE-FRANCE), XIV CENTURY

by comparison, for this is a superb group in an extraordinary state of preservation. Only the scepter which the Virgin held in her right hand and the tips of her crown are missing.

A white veil bordered with narrow green and red lines is drawn over the Virgin's golden hair, and one end is clutched in the right hand of the benign Child, who holds an apple in his left. The Infant's red tunic contrasts with that of the Virgin, which was formerly completely gilded. Her blue mantle, lined in green, is stenciled in gold to imitate brocade. The gold orphreys are studded with paste jewels.

For almost twenty years the statue was an outstanding possession of the Berlin Museum. It was sold when the museum was negotiating the purchase of the major portion of the Guelph Treasure. Previously it was in the collections of James Simon and Lord Caledon.

This statue is perhaps the finest of the fourteenth-century Madonnas from the Île-de-France. It is strikingly similar in form not only to the fragmentary Madonna at the right but to the Virgin and Child at Rampillon, near Provins. Also closely related are the best of the Louvre

FIG. 29. A BISHOP
WOOD, PAINTED AND GILDED
ITALIAN, XIV CENTURY

statues of this subject and a Madonna on the west wall of this gallery, both said to have come from la Celle, south of Paris.

OTHER SCULPTURES. The standing deacon with a book in his left hand (fig. 30), originally with the palm of martyrdom in his right, was once thought to belong to the group of apostles formerly in the chapel of Rieux at Toulouse and now in the Toulouse Museum. Although closely related to the Rieux sculptures, it is now certain that this figure is not one of them. The composure and serenity of these idealized statues place them apart from many of the more dramatic religious sculptures of the fourteenth century.

The grandeur of a bishop is strikingly represented in the standing figure who raises his right hand in blessing (fig. 29). The cope is ornamented with black orphreys on which are quatrefoils. In one God the Father is shown blessing; in those below, the letters of Ave Maria are placed against red backgrounds. This sculpture from the parish church of Monticchio, in the region of Aquila, is very similar to the

FIG. 30. A DEACON SAINT
LIMESTONE
FRENCH, XIV CENTURY

61

FIG. 31. THE MAN OF SORROWS
FRESCO BY A FOLLOWER OF NARDO DI CIONE
ITALIAN, XIV CENTURY

well-known fourteenth-century statue of a bishop in the Bar-
gello in Florence. Both figures are of wood, embellished with
the care given to a panel painting.

PAINTINGS. Over the lintel of the central doorway is a
fresco of Christ (fig. 31) from a Florentine monastery that
was razed to make way for a street. It may once have been used
above a door, as here, or as a lunette beneath an arch, possibly
in a niche above a tomb. This painting of the Man of Sorrows
is by one of the followers of Nardo di Cione (active about 1343,
died in 1365 or 1366), to whom Ghiberti ascribed the frescoes
in the Strozzi Chapel of Santa Maria Novella in Florence.

62

# THE EARLY GOTHIC HALL

Some scholars attribute the fresco at The Cloisters to Nardo's follower Niccolo di Tommaso.

An altarpiece showing the Intercession of Christ and the Virgin comes from the Cathedral in Florence. The Virgin recommends eight small figures to Christ, and Christ indicating his wound looks up at God the Father above. The Italian inscriptions are translated: "My Father, let those be saved for whom you wished that I suffer the passion," and "Dearest Son, because of the milk that I gave you have mercy on them." This painting is attributed to a late follower of Orcagna active in Florence about 1400.

The tempera painting The Adoration of the Shepherds is probably from an altarpiece (fig. 32). Charming in composition and in the handling of details and effective in coloring, this picture has a universal appeal. A product of the Sienese school of the middle of the fourteenth century, it is now ascribed to Bartolo di Fredi. In style it may be compared with the work of the followers of the Lorenzetti.

CEILING BEAMS AND WINDOWS. The beams in the ceiling of this room and the arch at the far end were suggested by similar architectural members in the reconstructed Salle des Chevaliers in the Porte Narbonnaise at Carcassonne. The beams, which were painted when they were used elsewhere, have been scraped and now have the appearance of beams from an old ceiling which have lost their polychromy.

The three windows in the west wall came from Beaumont-le-Roger, and the fourth, placed between this gallery and the Gothic Chapel, was formerly in the wall of a church at la Tricherie, near Châtellerault. These thirteenth-century windows afford an unusual opportunity for a close study of original mediaeval stonecutting. Here and there the three larger windows have been repaired, but the restorations are readily dis-

FIG. 32. THE ADORATION OF THE SHEPHERDS
ITALIAN, SIENESE SCHOOL, XIV CENTURY

tinguished. The fine profiles of the moldings, their freehand cutting, and the graceful lines should be compared with the mathematically exact creations of modern work in the Gothic style. It is not the breaks and weather-worn surfaces that make for the live quality of authentic mediaeval architecture but rather the straightforward design and the vigorous execution.

64

# THE GOTHIC CHAPEL

THE Gothic Chapel incorporates in its design features suggested by a small chapel in the church of Saint-Nazaire at Carcassonne and the church at Monsempron. This modern setting has been more completely developed than elsewhere in The Cloisters, in order to create an effective background for the objects exhibited. The capitals, however, are of the simple bell type, unornamented so as not to detract from the mediaeval stonework, and in the same spirit the modern stained glass that supplements the mediaeval French and Austrian panels (see pp. 77-79) has been kept as unobtrusive as possible.

The stone window (see p. 63) and the high doorway from the Cistercian abbey of Gimont are interesting examples of architectural stonework. At Gimont the doorway was used in a court, the monumental proportions giving due prominence to the opening. The delicate tracery at the top gives an idea of the quality of the original carving, which has suffered considerably from exposure to the elements and from vandalism. While not contemporary with the style of the chapel, this late fifteenth-century doorway is an appropriate entrance to the adjoining Fifteenth-Century Sculpture Hall.

THE EFFIGY OF JEAN D'ALLUYE. The thirteenth-century sepulchral effigy of Jean d'Alluye (fig. 33) came from the abbey of la Clarté-Dieu, near le Mans. It is a magnificent example of this type of sculpture and one of the few surviving in such fine condition. The figure is life-size and represents a young man, fully armed, lying with hands joined on his breast in an attitude of prayer. His feet rest against a small lion, symbolic of courage. In its conventional portrayal of the

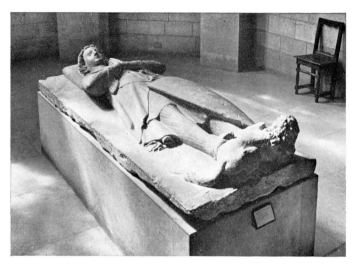

FIG. 33. THE SEPULCHRAL EFFIGY OF JEAN D'ALLUYE
FRENCH, XIII CENTURY

subject as youthful and with wide-open eyes this effigy exemplifies the idealism of thirteenth-century French sculpture.

Jean d'Alluye, Chevalier, Seigneur of Châteaux (later, Château-la-Vallière), Saint-Christophe, Chenu, Noyant, Méon, etc., was the son of Hugues V d'Alluye and his wife, Guiburge de Chourses (Sources). In 1240 he borrowed 150 livres tournois from the monks of the abbey of la Trinité at Vendôme to meet the expenses of a voyage to the Holy Land. In 1241, while in the East, he was given a relic of the True Cross by Thomas, bishop of Hierapetra. On his return to France in 1244 Jean d'Alluye gave the relic (now in the *hôpital* of Baugé) to the abbey of la Boissière. He died about 1248 and was buried in the abbey of la Clarté-Dieu. This monastery was founded in 1239 and constructed on land in the parish of Saint-Paterne, over which Jean d'Alluye held seignorial rights. The tomb with

66

the sepulchral effigy is said to have been erected in the church near the chapel of Saint Peter; on the wall behind the effigy was a bas-relief representing an abbot with several monks. According to another account, the tomb was in the cloister gallery near the entrance to the church. That it was used against a wall can be determined by the carving.

TOMBS OF THE COUNTS OF URGEL. The four monumental Catalan tombs came from the Premonstratensian monastery of Santa María de Bellpuig de las Avellanas, north of Lérida in Spain (figs. 34-36). They were erected at the end of the thirteenth or early in the fourteenth century by Armengol X, Count of Urgel (died 1314), in the Gothic church of Las Avellanas, a monastery founded in 1146 (or 1166) by Armengol X's ancestors, Armengol VII and his wife, Doña Dulcia, as a burying place for themselves and their family. As a result of the Spanish laws of 1835-1837 decreeing the sequestration of church properties, the monastery passed into private ownership. In 1906 the tombs were sold and the remains of the bodies were removed to the not too distant church of Vilanova de la Sal, a town founded by Armengol VII and once owned by the monastery of Las Avellanas.

The tomb of Armengol VII was erected in a niche in the presbyterium at the epistle side of the main altar of the church. Opposite, in a niche of similar architectural proportions to the one constructed for his forbear's tomb, Armengol X provided for his own eventual burial in a sarcophagus placed above the one made for Doña Dulcia. The fourth tomb, that of Don Alvaró de Cabrera the younger (died 1299), brother of Armengol X, was placed in a niche in a small side chapel of the church. The tombs were described in great detail by Jaime (Jacobus) Caresmar, abbot of Las Avellanas from 1766 until 1769 and a resident at the monastery from 1740 until his death in 1791, in a history of the monastery from its founding until 1330. In this work, based on original documents, Caresmar describes the opening of Alvaró's tomb in the year 1739. An old parchment found sewn to the linen cloth covering the bones stated that Alvaró's "spirit sought the stars in the year 1299" and that "Ermengaudus (Armengol) X, Count of Urgel, set up this monument to his very dear and deserving brother."

Don Alvaró was killed in the battle for Sicily, and in his effigy he is shown clad in full armor. A dog, wearing a collar decorated with bells, crouches at his feet. Two lions support the sarcophagus, on which the arms of Urgel are displayed.

The double tomb for Armengol X and for Armengol VII's wife, Doña Dulcia, is supported by two simple blocks (modern restorations after photographs of the originals, which have disappeared). The sarcophagus of Armengol X bears the arms of Urgel; Doña Dulcia's displays the arms of Foix and Urgel. On the slanting lids of the sarcophagi are effigies, the heads reposing on tasseled cushions incised with the arms of the departed; an angel holds the pillow under Doña Dulcia's head. Armengol's feet are placed on the back of a dog, symbol of fidelity and domesticity. Doña Dulcia's feet are placed as if she were standing; they are supported by a corbel which has a protecting griffin carved on its underside.

The tomb of Armengol VII is the most elaborate of the Urgel monuments. Three lions support the sarcophagus, which is ornamented on the front with carvings in high relief of Christ enthroned in majesty and of the twelve apostles. An arcade of trifoliated, pointed arches enframes the figures. In niches on the piers between the arches are small figures of angels and various saints. The ends of the sarcophagus are sculptured only in part, as the tomb was placed in a canopied niche from which it projected about half its depth. On the end to the spectator's right, two monks stand beneath a pointed arch which continues the arcade on the front of the sarcophagus. The arch is repeated on the corresponding end at the left, but the figures are omitted.

Armengol is represented lying extended on the sloping top of the sarcophagus lid. His head rests upon two tasseled cushions, the smaller wrought with the arms of Urgel—checky (15), gold and black. Behind his head is an angel. His hands are crossed above his sheathed sword; a lion crouches at his feet. Behind the effigy and forming part of the same slab of stone are small figures of mourners, many rows deep. Standing in front are ladies, draped in long cloaks, and knights, from whose shoulders hang swords; several couples on the left are seated. At the right, by the head of Armengol, is a cleric holding an open book before him; he is saying prayers for the dead. In the back rows are numerous figures wearing hooded mantles.

FIG. 34. THE TOMB OF DON ALVARÓ DE CABRERA (D. 1299)
SPANISH (CATALAN), 1299-1314

FIG. 35. TOMBS OF ARMENGOL X AND DOÑA DULCIA, WIFE OF
ARMENGOL VII. SPANISH (CATALAN), 1299-1314

FIG. 36. THE TOMB OF ARMENGOL VII, COUNT OF URGEL
SPANISH (CATALAN), 1299-1314

Unfortunately, this part of the tomb has suffered serious in-
jury, and few of the heads remain.

Part of the funeral rites, the absolution, is represented on
the superimposed panel, which is separated from the company
of mourners by a molding ornamented with leaf motives similar
to those carved on the front of the slab near the head of the
effigy. The figures in high relief carved on this upper panel are
much larger in scale than those below. The central group is
composed of three figures: the celebrant and two clerics in dal-
matics, who hold up a funeral pall in front of him. The celebrant wears the funeral cope; both arms have been broken off,
but there are indications that he probably held a crosier in his
left hand; the right was raised in benediction or may have held
the sprinkler for holy water. To the left of this group, a cleric
assisted by a young server holds a vestment, probably the chas-
uble which the celebrant removes after the requiem mass. Next
are a thurifer, carrying a censer and an incense boat, and two
assistants in copes. To the right of the central group are a deacon, a bearer of holy water (?), a thurifer, and three assistants
in copes. In the background are other members of the clergy.
Above the central group a small naked figure, representing the
soul of the deceased, ascends to heaven escorted by angels.

The effigy of Armengol VII is very similar to those of the
other Avellanas tombs, and all may be the work of one and the
same artist. His sarcophagus is related to the retable from
Anglesola, now in the Boston Museum, and to some sculptures
in the not too distant Cathedral of Tarragona. Various French
sculptors, including at least one from Tournai, who are mentioned in contemporary texts as working in Catalonia, have
been suggested as the link between the art of the North and
these Spanish monuments which show strong Northern influence. The Avellanas tombs are superior in quality to any of the
somewhat later Catalan monuments inspired by the Northern

style and may in part be the work of Northern artists. No definite assertion, however, as to the authorship of such mediaeval monuments should be attempted without the aid of more thorough documentation than is now available.

In execution the relief with the celebrants is different from and inferior to the effigy and the sarcophagus of Armengol VII. The supporting lions are somewhat coarser, although perhaps more architectural in feeling, and were probably not made by the sculptor or sculptors who worked elsewhere on the tomb. Such sculptures as these lions occur again and again in tombs and sepulchral monuments throughout Catalonia during the fourteenth century. Reliefs very similar to the one with the celebrants are also found elsewhere. It is possible, even probable, that such less important parts were "carried in stock" or made to order at various places. The assimilation of sculpture from different workshops would account for the use of stone from different quarries for the various parts of the same monument, as in the tomb of Armengol VII.

TOMB SLABS. By the thirteenth century the ever-increasing number of sepulchral monuments had begun to crowd the churches and chapels, and tomb slabs placed level with the floor were used extensively to mark places of burial. These slabs, sometimes made of metal, although more frequently of stone, were at first unornamented, except for a simple inscription giving the name of the deceased, the date of his death, and a conventional declaration of his virtues. In time the slabs became more and more elaborate. The fourteenth-century tomb slab of Clément de Longroy and his wife Beatrice de Pons, engraved in limestone and inlaid with white marble, is said to come from Aumale, near Dieppe. Clément is shown dressed in plate armor with a sword girded at his side; at his feet is a lion, and at either side of his head a shield emblazoned with his arms. His wife is portrayed in the costume of the day, with two small hounds at her feet. Her coat of arms is emblazoned at either side of her head. Parts of the Norman-French inscriptions may be translated as follows: "Here lies the noble man Messire Clément de Longroy, called . . . Christopher, Sire de Fontaines, Major-domo of the King . . . and of the Queen Blanche, who died in the year of grace one thousand—. Here lies the noble lady, Madame Beatrice de Pons, Dame de Fontaines, wife of the said . . . Christopher, who died in the year of grace one thousand—." The dates on this tomb slab were never completely inscribed, which suggests that the stone was cut before the decease of either Clément or his wife.

OTHER SCULPTURES. The two over life-size sculptures of Saint Margaret and another saint (figs. 37, 38), with their original canopies, are among the most grandiose and well preserved of monumental Gothic stone statues. They are carved in limestone. Removal of heavy coats of the later repaint that protected these figures has revealed their original polychromy. The extraordinary state of preservation of the colors— for example, the greens and reds richly bordered with gold, only traces of which remain—gives an excellent impression of the original condition of mediaeval sculptures. Even the necklace of the smaller figure was delicately painted and gilded. The ridged eyebrows are accented with dark paint which contrasts with the tawny flesh color.

These statues may be attributed to the Catalan school and to the third decade of the fourteenth century on the basis of their relationship to the recumbent figure of Teresa de Moncada Cervera in the Provincial Museum of Lérida. This effigy is from one of the tombs of the early fourteenth-century chapel of Saint Peter in the Old Cathedral of Lérida, now largely destroyed. The treatment of the hair, the folds of the Gothic

74

FIGS. 37, 38. SAINT MARGARET AND ANOTHER SAINT
PAINTED LIMESTONE. SPANISH, ABOUT 1330

draperies, the incised ornamentation of the borders of the garments, the modeling of the hands, the flat planes of the faces, and in particular the ridges of the eyebrows are character-istics common to the Moncada effigy and these two statues at The Cloisters. In some respects they recall the Avellanas tomb figures. While there is no evidence that the statues come from Lérida, the proximity of Las Avellanas to Lérida, some thirty miles, would alone explain the similarities of all the Catalan sculptures in the Gothic Chapel.

Notwithstanding its weathered surface, the monumental figure of a bishop has lost none of the dignity and solemnity originally portrayed by the sculptor (fig. 39). Statues of this quality are rarely seen except in their original architectural set-tings in well-known buildings. This sculpture was discovered in the thirties in a garden near Chablis. In many respects it resembles the figure of the patron saint on the trumeau of the north portal of the Burgundian church of Saint Thibault, to which the date 1305-1310 has been assigned. The bishop, a con-temporary work, also may have been placed on a trumeau at an entrance to a church.

Two angels, both originally holding candlesticks, have been placed on the corbels at either side of the tomb of Armengol VII (see fig. 36); the horsemen known to have been there in the fourteenth century have long since disappeared. These charming thirteenth-century sculptures recall the angels of the Coronation of the Virgin in the central doorway of Reims Cathedral, and, like the tomb of Armengol VII, they retain significant original polychromy. Formerly the angel at the left wore a green mantle with a red lining, fastened with a clasp over a gilded tunic. The hair was completely gilded, but only a few traces of the gold now remain over the brown underpaint. The flesh tints are particularly interesting, the red paint on the cheeks accentuating the angel's archaic smile.

76

THE STAINED GLASS. The mediaeval stained-glass panels in the Gothic Chapel have been supplemented by sections of modern glass which are an interpretation of the fourteenth-century grisaille in the center window. Without some patterned background the impression of light vibrating through semitranslucent glass, so to be remembered in many European churches, would not have been obtained. Stained glass painted in grisaille was used early in the Middle Ages as an expedient method for saving part of the great expense involved in filling vast windows with elaborately decorated glass. Especially in the north of France, where the light was not so brilliant as in southern districts, windows with the more translucent grisaille were sometimes preferred.

The lancet windows in the chapel were planned so that the two stained-glass panels with their contemporary grisaille could be placed in the apse (fig. 40). This glass is said to come from Évron, and on the basis of style it is dated in the first half of the fourteenth century. The figures closely resemble others in the cathedral of Evreux, which were made about 1330 and are

FIG. 39. A BISHOP. LIMESTONE
BURGUNDIAN
EARLY XIV CENTURY

universally considered to be among the finest examples of fourteenth-century glass.

On the panel at the left the prophet Isaiah (YSAIAS), wearing a cap and a green mantle thrown over a reddish brown tunic, is silhouetted against a bright blue background. He holds with both hands a scroll bearing the inscription ECCE VIRGO, taken from the prophecy *ecce virgo concipiet et pariet filium* (Behold, a virgin shall conceive, and bear a son. Isaiah 7.14) and frequently used in representations of him. On the other panel Saint Mary Magdalene is depicted with a red halo and draped in a red-brown cloak; her bare feet denote the penitent sinner. She holds her most usual attribute, an ointment jar. The saint is represented as weeping, with her head supported on her hand. This attitude of sorrow suggests the passage, "And they [the angels] say unto her, Woman, why weepest thou? She saith unto them, Because

FIG. 40. LANCETS WITH STAINED GLASS FROM ÉVRON FRENCH, XIV CENTURY

78

they have taken away my Lord, and I know not where they have laid him" (John 20.13).

The panel with Mary Magdalene bears the inscription M. MARTE. It would seem to have been partly restored at some time and a piece of old glass inscribed with the name of Martha, but from another window of the series, inserted. Or possibly the painter made an error and substituted MARTE for MAGDA. Martha was traditionally believed to be the sister of Mary Magdalene.

Stained glass which is brilliant in color, pleasant in subject matter, and careful in design is to be found in many small churches in Austria. It does not have the great vitality of much French glass, but it tells a story and is very decorative. The four panels inserted in the two other apse windows are Austrian work of about 1380. They represent Saint Bartholomew with knife and book, Saint John the Evangelist with chalice and serpent, and two scenes with Saint Martin dividing his cloak with a beggar.

Austrian panels of about the same period are inserted in another window. The panel with the Virgin of the Mantle sheltering six figures, including a bishop and a king, in a mandorla supported by four angels, comes from the church at Maria-Strassengel. The Annunciation and its associated canopy and the quatrefoil come from Ebreichsdorf, near Wiener-Neustadt. The companion piece of this charming, colorful panel is in the Kunstgewerbemuseum in Vienna.

FIG. 41. ARCADES OF THE BONNEFONT CLOISTER

# THE BONNEFONT CLOISTER

MOST, if not all, of the capitals on the two sides of the Bonnefont Cloister (fig. 41), and similar ones placed in the adjacent Trie Cloister, came from the former abbey of Bonnefont-en-Comminges. All are carved in gray-white marble from the quarries of Saint-Béat.

The abbey of Bonnefont-en-Comminges was founded in 1136 by six monks from the Cistercian abbey of Morimond on the invitation of Flandrine, widow of Geoffroi de Montpezat, and was favored by Roger de Nur, bishop of Comminges. When the monastery began to grow the counts of Comminges became its patrons, and until the middle of the fourteenth century they were buried there. The chapel was built in the second half of the twelfth century.

The cloister enclosure at Bonnefont was approximately rectangular. To judge from the buildings and traces of foundations still visible, it measured, including the walks, about 109 by 78 feet. Froidour described it in a letter written in 1667, saying, "All the columns are of marble and the ceiling [over the walks] is of paneled oak." It is not unlikely that the ceiling was added in the sixteenth century by Jean de Mauléon, bishop of Comminges, who was commendatory abbot of Bonnefont. Froidour stated further that "there is, on one of the four sides [on the south side near the refectory], a structure, approximately round, supported on columns similar to those of the cloister, in which there is a perfectly beautiful fountain . . . [that] furnishes water for the kitchen and wherever else it is required." Another account, written by Alexandre du Mège in 1807, relates that the cloister was still standing with its four galleries and 128 shafts, supporting capitals [this would mean sixty-four capitals], whose ornaments imitated both plants of

81

the region (see figs. 42, 43) and plants having no recognizable prototypes in nature.

During the nineteenth century most of the architectural sculpture from Bonnefont was dispersed. In fact, today there is scarcely a place of importance within twenty miles where there is not some vestige of the once celebrated monastery. A meandering, almost impassable wagon road now leads to the site of the former monastic buildings. Part of the largest one still standing is used by peasants for their farmhouse. Unfortunately, the records of existing sculpture have not been kept with sufficient care to permit positive statements as to the origin of individual pieces. A group of the capitals in The Cloisters collection was taken from Bonnefont about 1850 to Saint-Martin-sur-la-Noue (near Saint-Marcet) and was used to ornament the façade and gallery of a country house.

Twenty-one of the forty-eight double capitals, selected for their similarity in size and for the interest of their decoration, are installed in the two sides of the Bonnefont Cloister (see explanatory labels in the cloister). Five others have been incorporated in the arcade in the north wall of the Trie Cloister. Where necessary, a few new bases were made to supplement the old ones. Some of the shafts are original; others were probably made some years ago for the reconstruction of part of the Bonnefont cloister at the Déaddé house at Saint-Gaudens. Later, when the house was demolished, several of the arcades were erected in the public gardens at Saint-Gaudens, and these have been faithfully reproduced in the Museum's cloister. A fragment of an arch, which was taken from a rough stone wall near the original cloister at Bonnefont and used as a model for the profiles and the carving of the new arches, has been inserted in the second arch east of the Gothic Chapel.

The type of roof, with its beams and trusses, was suggested by the timber holes in the wall still standing on one side of the cloister at Bonnefont, and the treatment of the beams themselves is reminiscent of similar timber work in the former cloister at Marciac. The garden court (fig. 87), while not an archaeological reconstruction or one based on any particular prototype, was in a general way suggested by various examples depicted in paintings and related works of art (see pp. xxxiv f.).

Since all the archives of the abbey of Bonnefont were burned during the French Revolution, there is no documentary

FIGS. 42, 43. CAPITALS FROM BONNEFONT-EN-COMMINGES
FRENCH, LATE XIII-EARLY XIV CENTURY

evidence for the dating of the cloister. Coats of arms, among them those of the counts of Comminges and of Béarn, appear on some of the capitals, but as these escutcheons do not establish the period of their carving, the cloister can best be dated by comparing the capitals with those of other monasteries.

The capitals can be divided into two groups according to the style of their decoration, one comprising the capitals of simpler type, the other—which includes all the larger capitals —those with more sophisticated ornament. The first group is identical in style with capitals from the cloister of the Jacobins in Toulouse, whose conventual buildings were begun in 1294 and whose cloisters were completed in 1310. Moreover, the

83

arches of this cloister are like those which were used at Bonne-font-en-Comminges. The second group is identical in style with the capitals of the large cloister of the convent of the Augustinians at Toulouse (now the Musée des Beaux-Arts). This convent was built between 1310 and 1341 by brothers of the Augustine order. According to the existing document, in January, 1310, during a visit to the abbey of Bonnefont, Pope Clement V gave the Augustines—who then had their community outside the walls of the city of Toulouse, near the Mata-biau gate—permission to erect a new residence inside the city walls. From this evidence it may be concluded that the earlier style dates from the last decade of the thirteenth and the first decade of the fourteenth century and that the later style was developed about this time and continued through the first half of the fourteenth century.

# THE TRIE CLOISTER

IN 1571 the convent of Trie, except for the church, was destroyed by the Huguenots. Shortly afterwards some of the sculptured white and gray-white capitals from the cloister, and probably some from the near-by cloister of the monastery at Larreule, were sold to the Benedictine monastery of Saint-Sever-de-Rustan for the rebuilding of its cloister, which had also been damaged by the Huguenots. The cloister at Larreule has long since disappeared; according to some of the villagers, most of the sculpture and architectural stonework was used for the construction of a dam. Forty-eight of the capitals from Saint-Sever-de-Rustan, twenty-eight of which came originally from Trie, were sold in 1889-1890 by the commune to the city of Tarbes, capital of the canton of Bigorre. They were erected with their old arches and parapet copings in the Jardin Massey at Tarbes, where they are now preserved with pride.

Of the related capitals from Bigorre in the United States, twenty-three (eighteen of which are known to have come from Trie) are in The Cloisters. Others are in the collections of Stephen Carlton Clark and The Cleveland Museum of Art. The capitals, several old bases, and a section of an arch from Larreule, whose moldings were identical with those of the arches in the Jardin Massey, have helped make possible a reconstruction of three sides of a cloister at Trie (fig. 44; see also explanatory labels in the cloister). The fragment from Larreule has been inserted in the first arch of the west arcade. On the fourth side capitals from Bonnefont have been used (see pp. 81-84). The tiles, roof timbers, and ceiling were suggested by existing work of the period.

The capitals from the cloister at Trie are believed to have been carved between 1484 and 1490. The earlier date is established by the seventh capital of the west arcade, which is carved with the arms of Catherine, Queen of Navarre and Countess of Bigorre, quartering the arms of her husband, Jean d'Albret. The capital would not have been carved before the date of their marriage, June 14, 1484. The date 1490 is determined by a capital, not in The Cloisters, bearing an inscription referring to Pierre II, Cardinal of Foix (died 1490), as still living at the time the capital was executed.

Numerous coats of arms, perpetuating the names of local families, appear on the capitals. They are an indication of the increasing secularization of the arts in the late Gothic period. Grotesque subjects were also freely used, but the usual scenes from the Bible and legends of the saints predominate in the series. The historiated capitals do not represent all the scenes which might be expected, largely owing to the fact that of the eighty-one known to have been at Trie, only eighteen have been gathered together here.

The capitals have been placed in the west, south, and east arcades and have been arranged, wherever possible, according to the chronological order of the scenes represented, beginning at the northwest corner near the entrance from the Bonnefont Cloister. The most important subjects depicted are: *west arcade,* first capital, God creating the sun, moon, and stars (a sundial was at one time on the top face)—second capital, the creation of Adam; arms of La Barthe-Fumel; the creation of Eve—third capital, Abraham leading his son Isaac to the sacrifice; arms of Jean III, Count of Astarac; the sacrifice of Isaac—fourth capital, arms possibly of Algoursan; the same arms quartered with unidentified arms—fifth capital, armed boy and basilisk (fig. 45); Saint Matthew writing his gospel, with his symbol, an angel; arms of La Roche-Fontenilles—sixth capital, Saint John the Evangelist writing his gospel, with his symbol, an eagle; two children probably spinning tops with

86

FIG. 44. ARCADES AND GARDEN COURT OF THE TRIE CLOISTER

whips—seventh capital, arms of Catherine of Navarre supported by a bishop and Saint Anthony (?); arms of Ossun; Saint John the Baptist and a kneeling adorant, possibly Jean d'Albret, the husband of Catherine of Navarre—eighth capital, arms of Jean de Foix supported by John the Baptist and a female figure—*south arcade,* ninth capital, the Annunciation

FIG. 45. A CAPITAL FROM TRIE. FRENCH
PROBABLY ABOUT 1484-1490

to the Virgin Mary—tenth capital, the Nativity; the Annunciation to the Shepherds—eleventh capital, the Massacre of the Innocents; the devil tempting Christ to turn stones into bread —twelfth capital, unidentified arms—thirteenth capital, the burial of Lazarus; Martha and Christ; Christ raising Lazarus —fourteenth capital, Christ before Pilate; the Flagellation of Christ—fifteenth capital, the Entombment of Christ—*east arcade,* sixteenth capital, an adoring monk and the Virgin—seventeenth capital, Pentecost; Saint George killing the dragon— eighteenth capital, arms of the town of Trie or of Jean de Trie; Saint Michael overcoming the devil—nineteenth capital, Saint

88

# THE TRIE CLOISTER

Christopher holding the Christ Child, and a bishop; shield bearing symbols of the Virgin Mary; the monk Arnaldus and the Virgin Mary—twentieth capital, arms of France supported by angels; the stoning of Saint Stephen—twenty-first capital, Saint Catherine and Saint Margaret; the temptation of Saint Anthony—twenty-second capital, arms possibly of Arnaud d'Antin supported by a knight and a child with a hobbyhorse; arms of Cardaillac—twenty-third capital, Saint Martin sharing his cloak with a beggar; a woman with a distaff.

THE FOUNTAIN in the garden is composed of two late fifteenth- or early sixteenth-century limestone parts. On the front of the cross there is a figure of Christ between Mary and John; on the back Saint Anne, with the Child on her right arm and the Virgin at her left, stands between unidentified saints. The octagonal section is ornamented with seven apostles and John the Baptist in traceried niches; its original lead pipes issued from decorative heads just as the replacements do now. The shaft between the antique elements is modern, and the pedestal, of cast stone, is copied from the original in the Fifteenth-Century Sculpture Hall.

THE STATIONS OF THE CROSS set into the walls are appropriate to the Trie Cloister both in size and in subject matter, although they are in the renaissance style. The last relief of the series, with the Deposition, the Marys, and the *Noli me tangere,* still has traces of old paint and affords an interesting comparison with the other reliefs, showing to some extent the part played in sculptural effects by color as well as by weathering.

# THE FIFTEENTH-CENTURY
# SCULPTURE HALL

THE instability and violence of the times caused many artists of the fifteenth century to seek the protection of powerful patrons. Around the ambitious dukes of Burgundy there collected a brilliant entourage of artists, among them Claus de Werve and the great Claus Sluter. These sculptors,

with their associates and followers, helped to create the style known as Burgundian, whose influence spread far beyond the borders of the duchy. The changing political allegiances of the day prepared the way for the so-called International Style.

Although Sluter has been claimed as a native of the Lowlands, his birthplace is uncertain. The Well of Moses (1394-1404), the base for a Calvary in the Carthusian monastery of Champmol near Dijon, and the portal sculptures of the monastery's church are his best-known works. Two companion statues showing some of this master's salient characteristics are in the Museum's collections: a Saint

FIG. 46. BISHOP AND DONOR
PAINTED LIMESTONE
BURGUNDIAN, XV CENTURY

John (at 82nd Street) and the Saint James the Greater, with a cockleshell in his pilgrim's hat, in the Cuxa Cloister (see p. 46). His free forms, cloaked in yards of agitated drapery, foreshadow by a century the sculptural conventions of the end of the Middle Ages. Originally these statues must have been dramatically sumptuous with glistening gold applied over the entire surface, which was prepared with a red ocher underpaint. Only microscopic traces of the gold have survived.

A number of statues in the Burgundian style have been grouped together in the Fifteenth-Century Sculpture Hall. The variety of moods and ideas they express is characteristic of this period of expanding horizons. The bishop with a donor (fig. 46) is very similar to another worldly figure, the Saint Nicholas in the parish church of Moutiers-Saint-Jean. The introduction of donors, usually shown smaller in scale than the accompanying saints, was a favored practice towards the end of the century; sometimes vanity overcame modesty and the donors were portrayed life size or larger. The statue of Saint Denis, long a favorite saint in France, recalls numerous other statues, presented to churches and chapels, which show the same love of pomp exhibited in secular subjects. The portly burgher, an

FIG. 47. A BURGHER
LIMESTONE
FRENCH, XV CENTURY

91

unusual figure of unknown provenance, was no doubt drawn from life (fig. 47). It is possibly a Nicodemus or Joseph of Arimethea from an Entombment group.

The Saint Barbara holding her attribute, the tower where she was imprisoned by her father, who opposed her marriage, is a realistic representation of a demure maiden of noble family (fig. 48). Her gold tresses and her blue gown, enriched with silver, are remarkably preserved.

The Pietà was a subject introduced into France from the Rhineland, where it had become a popular object of devotion in the fourteenth century. A dramatic Rhenish group of this kind, produced in the last quarter of the fourteenth century, shows with restraint the seated Mother sorrowing over the body of Christ (fig. 49). The full folds of the drapery of the Virgin's robe, its gold borders enriched with jewels, are in striking contrast to the flat modeling of the arms and limbs of the prostrate figure. Another Pietà illustrates the unbroken continuity of the fourteenth-century style in the Île-de-France and Champagne during the early fifteenth century. The small

FIG. 48. SAINT BARBARA
PAINTED LIMESTONE
FRENCH, XV CENTURY

FIG. 49. PIETÀ. WOOD, PAINTED AND GILDED
RHENISH, ABOUT 1375-1400

size of the body of Christ in this work reflects the teachings of certain German mystics who believed that the Virgin, in the agony of her grief, imagined she was holding her dead son as a child again in her arms.

The larger than life size early fifteenth-century Italian Madonna and Child is in a very different mood from the Pietàs; the Mother smiles benevolently upon the carefree, spirited Child. Such sculptures, modeled in cloth made firm with glue and gesso, were light enough to be carried in proces-

93

sions through the streets on feast days. The green and red brocades of this Virgin's robe, enriched with winged beasts and intertwining ornament of gold, must have sparkled in the sun and candlelight. The group is said to come from the Convent of Santa Chiara in Vaglia Mugello in Tuscany.

A wave of prosperity in France, beginning in the second half of the fifteenth century, followed the re-establishment of peace and order, and the merchants of Champagne, enriched by the trade their bustling fairs stimulated, became leading patrons of the arts. The head of Christ crowned with thorns, carved in limestone, is executed with the sensitiveness characteristic of the school of Champagne, but the treatment is more restrained than in many other fifteenth-century representations of the subject. Two figures of holy women from an Entombment group represent the culmination of the Gothic style in Champagne. These figures, found embedded in a wall at Chartres, derive from the famous atelier of Saint Martha at Troyes and were carved between 1520 and 1530.

Gradually the ateliers of Champagne lost their vigorous traditionalism. Though previously their patrons had not been especially interested in Italian art, then fashionable in court circles, the sculptors soon sought to imitate the elegance of the North Italian styles which came into vogue in the first half of the sixteenth century.

Late mediaeval figures of saints are less austere in style than earlier representations and show the saints sharing the daily life of other men; saintliness is usually manifested by some supernatural occurrence in the midst of an ordinary occupation —Saint Hubert, for instance, is hunting when he encounters a stag with a crucifix between its antlers. This popular mediaeval miracle is illustrated by an impressive relief (fig. 50) in which all the incidental details of the legend are placed in a well balanced arrangement.

94

FIG. 50. SAINT HUBERT AND THE STAG
LIMESTONE, ONCE PAINTED. FRENCH, XVI CENTURY

STAINED-GLASS ROUNDELS (figs. 51-54) like
those in the windows of this gallery were very popular during
the fifteenth and sixteenth centuries, particularly in the Netherlands, Switzerland, and Germany. Although commonly they
represented sacred subjects, the roundels were used extensively
in secular buildings. It was customary to set such roundels in
leaded panes of clear glass.

The characteristic bright yellow color was produced by a
silver stain, which was fused on the outside of the glass. This
technique afforded new possibilities in the manufacture of
stained glass, for it permitted craftsmen to execute two-color
cartoons without using as many leads as were formerly required. At first a pale golden transparency was obtained, and
subsequently many shades between light lemon yellow and deep

95

amber were produced. The dark lines on the roundels were drawn on the inner surfaces and then fired in a kiln; afterwards details were sometimes accentuated, or patterns made, by scraping away portions of the opaque areas and exposing the glass.

The roundels show considerable variety in subject and in manner of presentation. Narratives from the Old and the New Testament and the apocryphal gospels—especially scenes relating to Christ's birth, passion, death, and resurrection—were illustrated. The story of Tobit and the parable of the prodigal son also were favored subjects. Incidents in the lives of saints and martyrs were frequently depicted, and sometimes a patron saint was represented. With the introduction of the Italian Renaissance into northern countries mythological and other classical stories became the fashion. As Gothic and renaissance details often appeared in a single panel, the dating of the roundels is exceedingly difficult. The style is often derived from manuscript illuminations and book illustrations. Artists noted for their drawings and paintings are known to have furnished designs for stained glass, particularly for some made at the centers of manufacture in Augsburg, Nuremberg, Cologne, and the Netherlands.

STAINED-GLASS PANELS. In the window looking towards the Trie Cloister are two stained-glass panels showing the kneeling figures of Wilhelm von Weitingen and his wife, Barbara von Zimmern, with their coats of arms. Both panels have flashed blue backgrounds, one with holly and birds, the other with hopvine and birds. This glass, dated 1518, was presumably made for the church at Sulz am Neckar, where the donors lived. It is said to have been owned for seven generations by a family named Meebold, who acquired it when the church was restored in the seventeenth century.

THE ADORATION OF THE MAGI        THE FLAGELLATION OF CHRIST

DANIEL KILLING THE DRAGON        THE PRODIGAL SON

FIGS. 51-54
STAINED-GLASS ROUNDELS. FLEMISH AND GERMAN
LATE XV-XVI CENTURY

FIG. 55. WOODWORK FROM ABBEVILLE. FRENCH
LATE XV-EARLY XVI CENTURY

THE ABBEVILLE WOODWORK. In the north of
Europe, where wood was plentiful, it was employed extensively
for building, often in combination with stucco. The elaborately
carved woodwork adjacent to the staircase (fig. 55) comes
from the courtyard of a house at Abbeville known as the
House of Francis I, although it was probably built in the reign
of his predecessor, Louis XII (1498-1515). The door at the
right originally opened on a spiral staircase, which led to the
second floor. The small figures on brackets probably represent
apostles and prophets. The initials on the panels have not as
yet been identified.

# THE TREASURY

CONSTANTINE collected gold and precious materials for the fashioning of sacred vessels, and the kings of France, as early as the sixth and seventh centuries, enriched the abbeys of Saint-Germain-des-Prés and Saint-Denis. As such possessions accumulated, abbeys and monasteries, cathedrals and churches, kings and nobles formed treasuries, where valued objects used for religious services and state occasions were placed for safekeeping. Sometimes church treasures were locked away in the crypt, but more generally they were placed in stout cupboards or in the thick walls of the sacristy, where the treasurer, who usually slept there, could guard them. Occasionally treasures were kept continuously on view for the faithful in the sanctuary. At Aix-la-Chapelle the so-called Charlemagne treasure, including a hunting knife and horn and a reliquary bust containing part of his skull, could be seen in the cathedral treasury; but the four great relics—"Christ's swaddling clothes and loin cloth, the shroud of John the Baptist and the Virgin's robe"—in the sumptuous silver-gilt Shrine of the Virgin were exhibited to the public only every seven years.

FIG. 56. MOUNT ON ONE OF THE DOORS TO THE TREASURY XI-XII CENTURY

Three rooms at The Cloisters have been set apart as the Treasury. Here are shown a small group of objects of exceptional quality from the Hermitage in Russia, from great art collections in Paris, and other sources.

99

THE WROUGHT-IRON MOUNTINGS of the eleventh or twelfth century on the modern oak doors at the entrance to the Treasury (fig. 56) were made for a church door at Saint-Léonard-de-Noblac in the south of France. They are close in design to eleventh-century manuscript illuminations of the region, particularly to two from the near-by monastery of Saint-Martial in Limoges.

THE WOOD PANELING. Thirty-seven elaborately carved oak panels representing scenes from the lives of the Virgin and of Christ have been set in the modern wainscoting in the anteroom (fig. 57). They are said to have been made about 1500 for the royal abbey of Jumièges in Normandy, perhaps to decorate the choir stalls ordered by the abbot Jacques

FIG. 57. WOOD PANELS WITH SCENES FROM THE LIFE OF CHRIST
FRENCH AND FLEMISH, EARLY XVI CENTURY

FIG. 58. THE NATIVITY AND THE VISION OF THE MAGI
DETAIL FROM AN ALTARPIECE. FOLLOWER OF VAN DER WEYDEN
SECOND HALF OF THE XV CENTURY

d'Amboise in 1501 or the choir screen also erected during his administration (1474-1504). They may have been sold when the abbey's rich furnishings were dispersed after the French Revolution. The panels were brought, early in the nineteenth century, by the British Ambassador to France, Lord Stuart de Rothesay, from Normandy to Highcliffe Castle in Hampshire, England, where they remained until 1950. They are the combined product of at least four master craftsmen who worked with the skill for which woodcarvers of Flanders and this region of France were famous at that time.

THE PAINTED ALTARPIECE has as its central theme the Nativity with God the Father above, surrounded by jubilant angels. On the left is the Vision of the Emperor Augustus, on the right the Vision of the Magi—both from

*The Golden Legend.* In the first of these scenes the Tiburtine Sibyl answers Augustus's question whether there was anyone alive as great as he by showing him a vision she beholds in the center of the noon-day sun, a maiden holding a child in her arms. In the other scene the Magi, after bathing and praying, behold in a star the Child, who directs them to Jerusalem where they will "find the son of the Virgin, God and Man, which was then born." The Visitation and the Adoration of the Magi are shown on the wings. The figures on the reverse of the wings, Adam and Eve and Saints John the Baptist and Catherine of Alexandria, are not visible when the retable is open.

This altarpiece was once in a convent in Segovia. Even though it lacks the original framework and two lower wings, it is extraordinarily well preserved. In large part it was inspired by Rogier van der Weyden's similar altarpiece, commissioned by Peter Bladelin, treasurer of Duke Philip the Good of Burgundy, about 1445 and now in the collections of the Kaiser Friedrich Museum.

THE CHALICE OF ANTIOCH. This chalice (fig. 59), made in the fourth, or possibly fifth, century for use in the sacrament of the Lord's Supper, is said to have been discovered in 1910 by Arabs digging a well near Antioch, one of the important early centers of Christendom in the East. Its simple, undecorated inner cup of silver is set in an openwork cup, also of silver, enriched with gilding. The openwork decoration consists of intertwined grapevines with birds and animals and twelve seated male figures—ten apostles and two representations of Christ on opposite sides of the cup. The shape was adapted from Roman examples. Both the figure and the ornament style are found after the third century in metalwork and stone sculpture.

This cup, one of several historic and distinguished liturgical

FIG. 59. THE CHALICE OF ANTIOCH
EARLY CHRISTIAN, IV-V CENTURY

chalices at The Cloisters, is probably the earliest known surviving Christian chalice. It has been the subject of a vast literature,
partly owing to an early and now unacceptable thesis that the
inner cup is none other than the Holy Grail used at the Last
Supper. It was exhibited at the International Exhibition of
Byzantine Art in the Louvre in 1931 and the Century of
Progress World's Fair in
Chicago in 1933-1934,
among other places.

THE BERTINUS CHAL-
ICE. The sturdy sacramen-
tal cup (fig. 60) was ham-
mered from heavy silver,
and the interior and rim were
gilded so that after cleaning
no drop of consecrated wine
would remain and the pre-
cious metals would glisten like
new. The pierced knob with
fantastic animals and foliage
allowed for a good grip and
concealed the fastenings of
the cup to the well-propor-
tioned base. The inscription cut in the silver-gilt band around
the bottom of the base, AD HONOREM B MARIE VIRGINIS
F BERTINUS ME FECIT A⁰ MCCXXII, states that the chalice
was made by Brother Bertinus in 1222. A similar though
smaller chalice in the Louvre, inscribed Pelagius, is thought to
be Spanish because the name Pelayo occurs in northern Spain.
The fact that there was a great abbey dedicated to Saint
Bertinus in the vicinity of St.-Omer in northern France suggests a provenance for the Bertinus chalice. However, although

FIG. 60. CHALICE
SILVER, PARCEL-GILT
BY BROTHER BERTINUS, 1222

FIG. 61. CHALICE, PATEN, AND STRAWS
GERMAN, SECOND QUARTER OF THE XIII CENTURY

related works have also been found in England, Iceland, and Scandinavia, no specific provenance for this chalice, even with its unusually complete inscription, has been ascertained. The chalice was first illustrated in 1896 when it was in the possession of Martin Hecksher in England; since then it has been in several exhibitions and in no less than three other private collections.

CHALICE, PATEN, AND STRAWS. This elaborate and rare early Gothic chalice, with the paten for the sacramental bread and straws for the sacramental wine (fig. 61), was purchased by order of Czar Alexander III in 1884 with the Basilewski collection in Paris and until the nineteen thirties was one of the treasures of the Hermitage. The set was made in the second quarter of the thirteenth century in Freiburg in Breisgau for the near-by abbey of Saint Trudpert. Saint Trud-

105

pert, a local saint, is portrayed below the figure of Christ on the paten. Around the bowl of the richly decorated chalice are Christ and the twelve apostles; around the knob are four New Testament scenes in gilded relief and on the foot the four related Old Testament scenes that prefigure them. The inscriptions and some of the figures are engraved, and the lines are filled with black niello, a hard compound of silver and sulphur, which contrasts with the brightly polished silver and gold. The chalice is enriched with amethysts, sapphires, turquoises, and garnets.

BOWL FROM A CIBORIUM. In his *Treatise upon the Various Arts* the monk Theophilus, whose tenth- or eleventh-century manuscript was widely copied, described the techniques for working gold, silver, copper, iron, stone, and wood that were followed in "industrious" Germany, as well as

FIG. 62. BOWL FROM A CIBORIUM
CHANNEL SCHOOL, XII CENTURY

the practices current in Italy, France, and Arabia. Niello, whose use he favored, is deftly combined with silver, parcel-gilt, in the ornamentation of a bowl (fig. 62), all that remains of a twelfth-century ciborium, made to hold the consecrated Host. The human figures, fantastic animals, foliage, and conventionalized designs in the decoration are fashioned with vigorous calligraphic feeling.

Though the bowl is similar in shape to that of the enameled ciborium of Alpais in the Louvre, typical of Limoges work (see p. 110), these two pieces differ in many respects. The bowl is ascribed to the Channel School because of its many similarities to works of art from centers close to the English Channel.

The bowl was purchased by Alexander Basilewski in the second half of the nineteenth century in an open market in Novgorod and in 1884 was sold with the Basilewski collection to the Czar for the Hermitage. A chalice of similar style and technique in the Stockholm museum was discovered by ditch-diggers in a pasture in Dune, in Gotland. The export of such European wares to the east and to the north from the eleventh century onwards was part of a general trade revival, chiefly among cities belonging to the Hanseatic League. Novgorod imported metalwork from the west in the twelfth and thirteenth centuries. Gotland established trading rights with Novgorod in 1229, with England in 1237.

RELIQUARIES. Pilgrimages across Europe and crusades to the Holy Land were occasioned by the cult of sacred relics. These venerated remains were often kept in containers wrought with the consummate devotion and skill of mediaeval craftsmen. One inventory alone—that made at Halle in 1520 for the treasury of Cardinal Albrecht of Brandenburg—illustrated three hundred and fifty reliquaries: one Byzantine, four Siculo-Arabic, eleven Romanesque, thirteen Gothic, and the others late Gothic and Renaissance. Crosses held fragments of the True Cross, heads or busts contained skulls, and other appropriate shapes were made to protect sacred bones; caskets, or boxes, of varying sizes and design also held venerated objects of all kinds. The examples acquired for The Cloisters contained no relics when they were purchased and now are of public interest only as works of art.

The RELIQUARY ARM of silver, parcel-gilt, with niello and jewels is in the style of Brother Hugo of Oignies, a famous goldsmith of Lorraine (fig. 63). One of his celebrated pieces from the treasury of the monastery of Oignies, now in the Institute of the Sisters of Notre-Dame at Namur, is dated 1228. More closely related, and perhaps by the same goldsmith, are the reliquary arm of Saint Landelin at Crespin, France, and another at the collegiate church of Saint Ursmer at Binche, Belgium.

The COPPER-GILT FIGURE now holding a reliquary cylinder formerly held a church in its hands (fig. 63). The embossed and tooled leather SHOE RELIQUARY was most probably a protective case for a metal reliquary that held a bone from a foot (fig. 63). The scenes from the life of Saint Margaret on this extraordinary piece from the Figdor collection in Vienna suggest that it contained a relic of this saint. As only slight traces of paint remain on the surface of the *cuir bouilli* (boiled leather), the coat of arms has not been identified.

The enameled Rhenish FLABELLUM of about 1200 (fig. 63) also once contained a relic behind the central filigree boss which opens on a hinge. Romanesque flabella are among the rarest and most spectacular ecclesiastical objects. These metal discs derived from the circular feather and parchment fans used in early mediaeval times to keep away flies during the celebration of the Mass. Often with cruciform decoration, they were carried like processional crosses or placed on the altar. They

FIG. 63. RELIQUARIES. XIII-XV CENTURY
ARM, LORRAINE, ABOUT 1230; FLABELLUM, RHENISH, ABOUT 1200
SHOE AND STANDING FIGURE, FRENCH, XIV CENTURY

FIG. 64. CANDLESTICKS, ALTAR CRUET, AND EUCHARISTIC DOVE
FRENCH (LIMOGES), XIII CENTURY

were sometimes carried in pairs. Stone statues in Cologne
Cathedral and in the Sainte-Chapelle in Paris are shown holding flabella. The metalwork of The Cloisters flabellum recalls
the cresting and filigree of the shrine of the Three Kings in the
treasury of Cologne Cathedral, the shrine of Charlemagne at
Aix-la-Chapelle, and the Mauritius shrine at Siegburg.

LIMOGES ENAMELS. In the twelfth and especially
in the thirteenth century the production of enamel and copper-
gilt work in Limoges in France attained the proportions of an
industry. Copper was available only a few miles from the city.

The EUCHARISTIC DOVE, symbol of the Holy Ghost, was
suspended above the altar and used for keeping the Host in
reserve (fig. 64). An unusual feature of this example is the
movable wings. The ALTAR CANDLESTICKS, one of two
enameled pairs at The Cloisters, retain their original gilding
(fig. 64). Altar cruets were also made in pairs for the Mass,
one for water, one for wine. The enameled CRUET shown here
is one of seven such cruets known to exist today (fig. 64).

Pairs of basins, one of which had a spout, were used for
washing at mealtime. They are called "gemellions," from the

Latin word meaning twin. The spouted BASIN is decorated with a coronation scene surrounded by merrymakers; the other BASIN shows a knight on horseback surrounded by knights on foot.

BRONZES. No group of mediaeval bronzes is more fascinating than the containers for water known as AQUAMANILES (see fig. 66). An inventory of about 1150 for the treasury of Mainz Cathedral describes "ewers of various shapes, called *manilia* because water is poured from them on the hands of the priests. Some have the shape of lions, others of dragons, birds, griffins, and other animals." To what extent these animals were symbolic and whether aquamaniles were used for domestic purposes is not certain. Mediaeval bronze workers were adept in casting and refinishing various metals, using their media boldly. The combination of zinc with copper made a readily workable alloy.

FIG. 65. CLASP. STYLE OF NICHOLAS OF VERDUN FROM THE REGION OF THE MEUSE, ABOUT 1200

Like modern brass, this so-called *auricalcum* glistens like gold when it is polished. Though it has not been customary in museums to clean mediaeval bronzes, those at The Cloisters have been restored as nearly as possible to their original condition. To avoid further tarnishing and the need for constant polishing, these objects have been given coats of preservative lacquer.

The CLASP of gilt-bronze (fig. 65) was surely made in the region of the Meuse about 1200, although, curiously enough, a silver-gilt buckle identical in style was found at Dune. The clasp may illustrate the text "Thou shalt tread upon the lion and adder: the young lion and the dragon shalt thou trample under feet" (Psalm 91.13). A few of these small objects are of such masterful execution that enlarged photographs of them reveal the plastic qualities of fine monumental sculpture.

The bronze BIRD, originally gilded, was found in Italy in 1925 (fig. 67). It has been published as an imperial eagle made

FIG. 66. AQUAMANILE
GERMAN, XII OR XIII CENTURY

to surmount the staff of Frederick II, Holy Roman emperor and king of Germany, Naples, and Sicily, but it more closely resembles a falcon, possibly a gerfalcon, the falcon of kings. Frederick, who established his court in Naples in 1220, was an enthusiastic falconer and wrote the standard mediaeval text on falconry. However tempting it may be to associate this bird with Frederick or with one of his predecessors who are known to have held staffs with eagles, the possibility

that it was part of some architectural monument or a
furniture mount cannot be
discounted.

## COVERED BEAKERS.

In the later Middle Ages the
increasing prosperity of the
merchants permitted them to
vie with the nobility in the
luxury of their daily life and
the lavishness of their gifts to
the Church. Two sumptuous
covered beakers (fig. 68) were
probably made as presentation
cups for the Town Hall of
Ingolstadt, north of Munich,
about 1470 by Hans Greiff,
the town's leading goldsmith.
An enamel plaque bearing
the coat of arms of the city is
fastened to the interior of the

FIG. 67. BIRD. GERMAN OR
ITALIAN, XI-XIII CENTURY

cover of the engraved beaker; the other has an Ingolstadt hall
mark. Both were sold after the Napoleonic wars; by 1863 the
engraved beaker was in the possession of a local druggist, and
the other also was privately owned in Ingolstadt. Both were
acquired later in the nineteenth century by the Frankfurt collector Carl von Rothschild.

These silver cups, parcel-gilt, were once even more elaborate
when all the beads, enameling, and paint were intact. Supporting the simpler of the two beakers are three armored knights
holding painted shields with bearded heads (restored), the arms
of Burgomaster Hans Glätzle of Ingolstadt. His portrait head

FIG. 68. COVERED BEAKERS

GERMAN (INGOLSTADT), SECOND HALF OF THE XV CENTURY

above a modern helmet, not illustrated, surmounts the finial. The shields of the engraved cup, held by "wild men," are bare, but were probably painted with the donor's arms. The foliate finial was originally entirely painted and enameled in naturalistic colors. The deep engraving on the flat surfaces recalls the style of the prints of the Master E. S.

NOTE. Textiles are shown in the adjoining room.

Visitors may reach the main floor by taking the staircase at the east end of the Fifteenth-Century Sculpture Hall.

# THE BOPPARD ROOM

THE STAINED GLASS. The six stained-glass panels from the church of the Carmelite convent of Saint Severinus at Boppard, on the Rhine, form the most brilliant ensemble of mediaeval stained glass in this country (see fig. 69). While this is not the finest glass the Middle Ages produced, the fact that it has been possible to obtain, almost intact, large panels of such fine quality is remarkable. Comparatively little of this fragile material has survived.

These panels appear to have been made for the polygonal choir of the church, which was part of the second oldest Carmelite house in Germany, founded before 1270. On the basis of style and various dates in the history of the church, they may be assigned to the second quarter of the fifteenth century. After the secularization of church property in the Rhineland in the Napoleonic era, the glass was sold. Not being fashionable, it was packed away until 1871. In 1875 it was acquired and restored by Frédéric Spitzer of Paris. At the famous sale of the Spitzer collection in 1893, it was again sold, together with other panels, and since then, except for the brief period in which it was on exhibition at the Musée des arts décoratifs, in Paris, it has not been on public view.

The six saints standing in elaborate canopied niches represent, from left to right, a bishop saint with a key and a crosier, trampling on a dragon symbolic of evil; the Virgin, with ears of wheat on her robe, and at her side an angel with a crown of flowers and a prisoner in a tower; another bishop saint; Saint Catherine of Alexandria with the attributes of her martyrdom, a wheel and a sword; Saint Dorothea of Caesarea holding a basket of red flowers from the celestial garden and at her side the Infant Christ; and Saint Barbara carrying her attribute, a

FIG. 69. STAINED GLASS FROM BOPPARD
RHENISH, SECOND QUARTER OF THE XV CENTURY

tower. In the lower sections there are the archangel Michael trampling a dragon and weighing souls; a silver shield with a red key; a pilgrim saint and Saint James the Greater and in the lower corners heraldic shields bearing emblems (*Hausmarken*); the arms of a guild of coopers—a red shield with a golden compass, two silver mallets, and a golden barrel hung beneath—held by two angels; a representation of the Holy Trinity; and two angels supporting a red shield with a silver star. The colors predominating in the windows are red, blue, golden yellow, and shaded white. The white turreted canopies are silhouetted against red or blue sky colors, which also appear in the side panels of the niches and contrast strongly with the white mantles the saints wear; spots of green and purple are scattered throughout, especially in the costume accessories and the narrow borders.

THE SPANISH ALABASTER RETABLE is appropriately shown with the stained glass from Boppard, for Rhenish artists were active in Spain in the fifteenth century. This retable (fig. 70), purchased in Paris by J. Pierpont Morgan, who presented it to the Museum in 1909, comes from the Archbishop's Palace in Saragossa. The variegated alabaster of which it is made has acquired a yellow tone. Such alabaster is frequently seen in sculpture from northern Spain, where it was quarried extensively along the Ebro river.

Traces of paint indicate that the canopied gables were originally rich with polychromy. The scenes below represent Saint Martin dividing his cloak with a beggar, Christ appearing to Saint Martin, the day of Pentecost (the descent of the Holy Spirit upon the apostles in the form of tongues of fire), the miraculous escape of Saint Thecla, a convert of Saint Paul, from death at the stake, and Saint Thecla listening to Saint Paul preaching. A painting may once have surmounted the

FIG. 70. ALABASTER RETABLE FROM THE ARCHBISHOP'S PALACE
IN SARAGOSSA. SPANISH, XV CENTURY

stonework. The panel with the instruments of the Passion and
the two figures holding heraldic shields bearing the arms of
Don Dalmau de Mur, who became archbishop of Saragossa in
1434, have been incorporated in an altar constructed in accord-
ance with a photograph of the original altar in the Archbishop's
Palace. The retable is well known in the literature of Spanish
sculpture. It recalls the great retables of the sculptor Pedro
Juan (active 1434-1445?) still standing in Saragossa.

WOOD SCULPTURE. A painted wood statue of Saint
Stephen (fig. 71), holding the stones of his martyrdom in the
folds of his garment, is attributed to the German sculptor,
Hans Leinberger, who is recorded as active between 1513 and
about 1528. The figure, with its architectural framework, recalls the stone sculptures placed beneath canopies on the exterior
of many churches and the figures in the stained-glass win-

dows from Boppard. Lein-
berger's work foreshadows
the baroque style.

## THE CEILING. The
painted section of the pine
ceiling comes from the Tyrol
and is of the late fifteenth or
early sixteenth century. The
monogram of Christ, IHS, in
the central panel suggests
that the ceiling was originally
used in an ecclesiastical, not
a secular, building, although
such ceilings are more usual
in domestic interiors.

## THE DOORWAY. The
entrance to the Hall of the
Unicorn Tapestries is marked
by an impressive limestone
doorway with a pointed arch
decorated in the flamboyant
Gothic style. Its strong arch,
composed of large stones laid
in eleven courses and held in

FIG. 71. SAINT STEPHEN
GERMAN, FIRST HALF OF
THE XVI CENTURY

place by a keystone, is gracefully carved with bases and column-
like moldings that emphasize the outline of the opening. The
superstructure is ornamented with cusps and pinnacles that
enhance the feeling of verticality. The two parallel cornices at
the top provide a transition to the wall above. Although this
upper part of the doorway has the appearance of a lintel, it is
the arch that carries the load of the wall.

119

# HALL OF THE UNICORN TAPESTRIES

THE Hunt of the Unicorn, a series of six tapestries and fragments of another, is among the most prized of our inheritances from the Middle Ages (see figs. 72-77). In design, in beauty of coloring, and in intensity of pictorial realism these hangings form the most superb ensemble of late mediaeval tapestries in existence.

Five of these tapestries were in all probability made for Anne of Brittany (1476-1514) in celebration of her marriage to Louis XII (1462-1515) on January 8, 1499, the marriage by which Anne, widow of Charles VIII, became queen of France for the second time. The two tapestries on the window wall—somewhat later in date and representing the first and seventh scenes in the series—may have been added to the original set when Francis I (1494-1547) married Anne's daughter and heir in 1514. All seven tapestries, possibly presented by Francis to his godfather, François de la Rochefoucauld, belonged to the Rochefoucauld family for generations.

The tapestries are first mentioned in an inventory of 1728 which states that they were at that time in the château of Verteuil, one of the ancestral seats of the Rochefoucauld family. Five of the tapestries hung in the great room of the new wing, and two others were in the great lower hall near the chapel. During the French Revolution they were taken from the castle and, according to one account, used for a time to protect potatoes from freezing. Portions now missing from the original fabric of the tapestries (see p. 125) were probably cut away in 1793 when the Société populaire of Ruffec sent to the Société populaire of Verteuil an edict ordering that all the paintings at Verteuil and all the tapestries having royal insignia be destroyed. In the nineteenth century the tapestries

FIG. 72. THE UNICORN AT THE FOUNTAIN
TAPESTRY IN THE SERIES CALLED THE HUNT OF THE UNICORN
FRANCO-FLEMISH, ABOUT 1500

were once again acquired by the Rochefoucaulds. They remained at Verteuil until the early twenties of the present century, when they were purchased by John D. Rockefeller, Jr., who cherished them in his New York residence until he presented them to the Museum for The Cloisters.

The unicorn, the fabulous and picturesque animal depicted in these tapestries, appears in the ancient folklore of India and the Near East. Ctesias, a Greek physician of the early fourth century B.C., described it, for the first time in literature, as an animal "exceedingly swift and powerful," which "no creature, neither the horse nor any other" could "overtake." The elder Pliny described it as an "exceedingly wild beast," with one black horn two cubits long projecting from the middle of its forehead, which, by reputation, could not be "taken alive." In the Middle Ages it was believed that the unicorn could be caught only by a virgin. It was related that this wild and unconquerable animal became tame when confronted by a maiden; he would lay his head in her lap and was thus easily taken by the hunter. The story is told in various versions of the *Physiologus*, a zoölogical and botanical encyclopaedia popular in Europe from the fifth century on, and in the bestiaries based upon it. In these accounts the unicorn is a symbol of Christ, the virgin is the Virgin Mary, the huntsman is the angel Gabriel, and the story of the hunt is an allegory of the Incarnation. Beginning with Richard de Fournival's *Bestiare d'amour* in the thirteenth century, there was an increasing tendency to interpret the legend of the unicorn caught by a maiden as an allegory of courtly love. In view of the fact that the Unicorn tapestries are thought to have been woven as a wedding gift, it is reasonable to suppose that at least one of the themes running through the elaborate portrayal of the hunt is the secular one of courtship and marriage.

Many allusions to the courtship and marriage of Anne and

FIG. 73. THE UNICORN TRIES TO ESCAPE
TAPESTRY IN THE SERIES CALLED THE HUNT OF THE UNICORN
FRANCO-FLEMISH, ABOUT 1500

FIG. 74. DETAIL FROM FIGURE 73

Louis may be found incorporated in the Hunt of the Unicorn. Prominent in the design is Anne's cipher 𝒜𝐸, the letters A and E (with the E reversed), the first and last letters of Anne's name and also of her motto, *A ma vie*. These letters, tied with a cordelière, a twisted cord or rope, appear on the average of five times in each of the six complete tapestries and once in the fragments. The same letters without the cordelière appear on one of the dog collars, and the letter A alone appears on two dog collars. The cordelière was worn by Saint Francis of Assisi, and Franciscan monks were called Cordeliers. Francis, Duke of Brittany, Anne's grandfather, used this emblem in evidence of his devotion to his patron saint. Anne also used it in every possible way; it appears with her arms, with the letter A in decorations, and as part of her dress. In 1498 she founded the chivalric order of the Dames de la Cordelière, which she bestowed upon the principal ladies of her court. Louis's colors, red and white (silver), are used in the cordelières in the five tapestries made for Anne.

To judge from a small fragment of original border in the third tapestry, The Unicorn Tries to Escape, all of the tapestries were framed as they are at the present, with two narrow bands of white and red and an outer band of shaded blue, the traditional color of royal France. These borders, which were replaced by modern copies in 1937, and other arms and insignia which may have been displayed where areas of the original sky are missing, were probably cut away following the edict of Ruffec in 1793.

The first tapestry shows the hunters, with varlets holding the dogs in leash, setting forth in search of the unicorn. A small figure in the upper right-hand corner is beckoning to his followers, probably to tell them that the unicorn has been sighted. The principal figure (the second from the left) is a young man of about twenty, probably Francis I, wearing the royal colors of France, red, white, and blue. He is accompanied by two companions carrying spears and wearing his colors, red, tan (yellow), and blue. The millefleurs background, a flowery mead on the edge of a forest, is elaborated with a variety of plants typical of late fifteenth- or early sixteenth-century tapestries; these are drawn with a freedom and grace entirely lacking in the rigid, comparatively expressionless figures. In this and the other tapestries in the series there are over a hundred distinct kinds of plants, about eighty-five of which are identifiable. They recall Anne's particular interest in flowers. Charles VIII planted gardens for her at Amboise, and Louis XII built other gardens for her at Blois.

In the second tapestry (fig. 72) the hunters have surrounded the unicorn, which kneels and dips its horn in a stream flowing from a fountain, a symbol of the waters of eternal life. This scene is described in the Greek bestiaries and is based on the old belief that the unicorn's horn would absorb poison. John of Hesse, who went to Jerusalem in 1389, records: "And even in our times it is said, venomous animals poison the water after the setting of the sun, so that the good animals cannot drink of it, but in the morning after the sunrise, comes the unicorn and dips his horn into the stream driving away the poison from it. . . . This I have seen for myself." The animals included in the tapestry are a lion and a lioness, a panther, a civet, a hyena, a stag, and two rabbits. These animals are themselves symbolic; for example, the lion stands for the strength of Christ, the panther for his sweet savor, and the stag, destroyer of snakes, for his power over evil. Perched on the rim of the fountain are two pheasants, a European goldfinch, and a swallow.

In the third tapestry (fig. 73) the unicorn tries to escape but is surrounded by the spearmen who approach from all sides. Anne's flag, which bears a black cross on a white (silver) field,

126

FIG. 75. THE UNICORN DEFENDS HIMSELF
TAPESTRY IN THE SERIES CALLED THE HUNT OF THE UNICORN
FRANCO-FLEMISH, ABOUT 1500

flies from a gable of the castle in the background. The dog collars with A and E and one with Louis's three silver-gilt fleurs-de-lis, the royal insignia, on a red band identify the dogs' owners. The monogram ℱℛ, noticeably different from the others actually woven in the tapestries, may be the initials of François de la Rochefoucauld or Francis I (Franciscus Rex). The only surviving fragment of the original border is to be found at the lower left-hand corner of this tapestry.

In the fourth tapestry (fig. 75) the unicorn, at bay, gores a greyhound with its horn. Anne is heralded in the inscription AVE REGINA C[OELORUM], the salutation to the Virgin, the Queen of Heaven, on the scabbard of the hunter at the extreme left. On the collar of the dog at the right of this huntsman is the corresponding salutation to Louis, O F[R]ANC[ORUM] RE[X].

In the fifth tapestry, of which only fragments remain, the hand of the virgin is shown grasping the neck of the unicorn, while a half-concealed huntsman signals with his horn to the other pursuers. The sleeve of the maiden is made of the same brocade as the dress worn by Anne in the sixth tapestry. The figure behind the unicorn is one of Anne's attendants. The introduction of Anne in this scene as the maiden who makes possible the capture of the wild beast also associates her with the Virgin in the Christian allegory of the Incarnation. The monogram of Christ, IHS, on one of the dog collars bears witness to the designer's intention of using the unicorn as a symbol of Christ in this story.

In the sixth tapestry (fig. 76) the unicorn is slain and brought to Anne and Louis, who appear life size, standing arm in arm in front of the castle. Though these are not portraits according to present-day conceptions, they bear striking resemblances to other contemporary representations of Anne and Louis. Anne and her ladies in waiting wear the characteristic

FIG. 76. THE UNICORN IS BROUGHT TO THE CASTLE
TAPESTRY IN THE SERIES CALLED THE HUNT OF THE UNICORN
FRANCO-FLEMISH, ABOUT 1500

Breton headdress of the period. Unlike other queens of France, who wore white for mourning, Anne, as in this tapestry, wore a black undercap. The gold chain with a pendent cross around her neck, the yellow-brown, red, and gold brocade of her dress, the brown fur, probably sable, lining her wide sleeves, the blue girdle, and the rosary attached thereto are familiar attributes of Anne as she is shown in other pictures. These items are also noted in extant inventories and expense accounts. The squirrel which is so prominent in the lower left-hand corner of the tapestry is actually held by Anne in other representations and may have some special significance that is not as yet apparent.

The colors of Louis's costume are particularly striking. The king wears a white hat, a short red robe or dress, and red and white striped stockings. After his marriage to Anne, Louis added her color, white, to his own, which had been red and yellow, and often used red and white exclusively. Among the several flags flying from the castle buildings the one to the left, above the figure of the queen, again shows a black cross, this time on a yellow and gold ground. From the next roof flies Louis's flag with a rather haphazardly drawn red porcupine on a field of white (silver). At the far right are two pennants bearing Louis's colors.

The seventh tapestry (fig. 77) can be interpreted as a symbol of the risen Christ. It shows the unicorn alone, alive but with his wounds apparent, within an enclosure probably signifying the *hortus conclusus,* a symbol of the Blessed Virgin and the Incarnation. Since the unicorn is leashed with a golden chain, symbol of marriage, to a tree bearing pomegranates, symbols of fertility, this tapestry is also to be interpreted as the consummation of marriage.

The tapestries are in an excellent state of preservation. The original weaving, except here and there, and then only in comparatively small, restricted areas, is almost as fresh as it

FIG. 77. THE UNICORN IN CAPTIVITY
TAPESTRY IN THE SERIES CALLED THE HUNT OF THE UNICORN
FRANCO-FLEMISH, ABOUT 1515

was the day the tapestries left the looms. There are occasional restorations of unknown date; the need for repairs is indicated in the inventory of 1728. The restorations, other than those executed under the Museum's supervision, seem to be eighteenth- or nineteenth-century work.

The subject matter is more appealing and the execution more vigorous than in most other works of art of the period. The individual scenes are treated pictorially, in each case fulfilling the requirements of the composition without too consistent an emphasis on perspective; but the individual figures, flowers, birds, and animals are naturalistically rendered (see fig. 74). The velvets and brocades of the costumes, the costume accessories, the dog collars, and other details are executed with many refinements of technique. The profusion of details and the harmonious colors are masterfully arranged. The distribution of the reds, yellows, blues, and orange, together with the emphasis on the white unicorn is as dramatic as it is pleasant; and the green and blue-green foliage is deftly worked into the background. The painstakingly prepared vegetable dyes allowed a range in color rarely surpassed in the most elaborate contemporary paintings and manuscript illuminations. Silver and silver-gilt threads are but sparingly employed, and then only to enrich certain details. The closely woven wool and silk threads (varying from about 16 to 19 ribs to the inch) produce an effect obtainable in no other medium.

It is as extraordinary as it is regrettable that it has not yet been possible to discover precisely by whom and where these tapestries were made. With works of such excellence it may also seem incredible that the artists who created them should not have been identified. There have been many attempts to establish a French or a Flemish origin for these tapestries, but no evidence sufficient to permit a declaration as to the place in which they were produced has been forthcoming. That the

# HALL OF THE UNICORN TAPESTRIES

Unicorn tapestries at The Cloisters bear strong resemblances to such hangings as the millefleurs tapestries depicting concert scenes in the Gobelins Museum, the Louvre, and the museum of Angers is certain. They also recall such hunting tapestries as those of the Duke of Devonshire at Hardwicke Hall, England, and the Lady with the Unicorn series in the Cluny Museum in Paris. All these tapestries have definitely Flemish characteristics, and at such centers as Tournai in the fifteenth century there was unprecedented activity. While the Cluny tapestries, generally ascribed to the Loire Valley, are closer than any others to the first and seventh of the Museum's series, none of the comparable tapestries are like the five tapestries made for Anne.*

MANTELPIECE AND WINDOW. A monumental fifteenth-century mantelpiece from Alençon is installed in the south wall. Opposite is a window from a late Gothic house in Cluny. In addition to the leaded glass in this window, described below, there are sheets of modern glass specially made to filter out the deleterious rays of the sun.

STAINED GLASS. Little evidence of the use of heraldry survives in the Unicorn tapestries; its fullest development, however, is represented in an unusual set of stained-glass panels (see fig. 78). Four of these panels contain the armorial achievements of the Emperor Maximilian; his son, Philip the Fair, King of Castile; his grandson, the young Prince Charles (later the Emperor Charles V); and one of his councilors, Henry, Count of Nassau. Another panel, not exhibited, shows the arms of Maximilian's chamberlain, Roland Le Febure, Lord of Tamise and Viscount of Haerlebeque. All five were living

* For further details see the *Bulletin of The Metropolitan Museum of Art,* Summer, 1942.

during Philip's reign (1504-1506), and the panels were probably painted at that time.

It is believed that the glass was made for one of Maximilian's residences — possibly for the Cour des Comtes at Ghent, the principal royal castle in Flanders. The two court officials honored in the glass were Flemings, and all the royal personages it commemorates are closely associated with the Cour des Comtes. Maximilian stayed there; Philip lived there except when he was in Spain; and Charles was born and spent his boyhood there —in fact, he was living there when the glass was painted.

FIG. 78. STAINED GLASS
WITH THE ARMS OF
THE EMPEROR MAXIMILIAN
FLEMISH, ABOUT 1504-1506

In these panels the delicate, transparent colors are combined with the strong outlines of the leading in an unusually harmonious arrangement. They also show a most accomplished use of several techniques: flashing with various yellow stains; cutwork, in which the glass is rubbed with hard stone; and the insertion of glass within glass by adroit leading. Except in the more complicated shields, the heraldic details are stained or stained and painted in black, yellow, white, and red on single panes of white glass. Such glass depends for effect more upon painting than upon the juxtaposition of small pieces of molded glass in various colors, the technique used in earlier periods.

# THE BURGOS TAPESTRY HALL

THE large tapestry in the Burgos Tapestry Hall is one of a series representing the Salvation of Man. The set is believed to have consisted of eight tapestries and to have been reproduced several times from the same cartoons. This is the only known tapestry of the series showing the Nativity and related subjects (see fig. 79). Also from Burgos Cathedral and now in the main building of the Museum is another tapestry of this series, The Redemption of Man, illustrating allegories of the conflict of Vices and Virtues.

According to tradition, these magnificent tapestries were woven in Brussels about 1495 for the Emperor Maximilian, who presented them to his son, Philip the Fair, to commemorate his marriage with Joanna, the daughter of Ferdinand and Isabella, in 1496. The double eagle of the Holy Roman Empire, woven in a prominent place, lends credence to this story. Furthermore, it is recorded that Pieter van Aelst, the famous tapestry weaver and dealer of Brussels, went to Spain with Philip on his first visit in 1502 and that, after the death of Philip at Burgos in 1506, Van Aelst was imprisoned by Ferdinand for taking some of Philip's tapestries and putting them in what he called a safe place. It is known that the streets of Burgos were hung with tapestries when Philip and Joanna came there in 1506 and that Van Aelst, with four assistants, was in charge of decorating the abodes of the royal couple, but it has not yet been possible to determine how and when the Nativity tapestry and three others of the series came into the possession of Burgos Cathedral. The great similarity of these tapestries to other productions of the Van Aelst workshops suggests their attribution to this great weaver, who is celebrated for having been entrusted with the making of tap-estries from cartoons by Raphael some years after the death of Philip.

The various scenes represented in the Nativity tapestry are arranged in two registers. In the upper register, at the far left, is shown God the Father, wearing a crown and holding a scep-ter, with figures denoting Humility and Charity; at the right Peace and Justice are embracing. Next is God the Father, en-throned and surrounded by figures, including Truth and Hu-mility, who hold a mirror in which is seen the Virgin kneeling in adoration before the young Christ Child. At the right the angel of the Annunciation holds a banderole inscribed with the salutation to the Virgin, who stands beside him. Other virtues and angels are included in the group. In the third scene Joseph, accompanied by Mary, presents the Roman tax collector with "a penny in acknowledgment that he was sub-ject to the empire of Rome," as recorded in *The Golden Leg-end*. In the fourth scene the Virgin is surrounded by the three figures of the Trinity; at the left the angel of the Annuncia-tion kneels before Humility. At the far right are three astrol-ogers of the East studying the prophecies of Balaam and beyond them the three Magi beneath the star in which they see the Child.

In the first scene of the second register Man, in fetters is shown with Nature, Misery, Hope, Abraham, Isaac, and Jacob. In the background is Temptation, holding a spear in one hand and a key in the other. The central group depicts the marriage of the Virgin Mary and Joseph. In the fore-ground of the third scene is the Christ Child and behind the kneeling Virgin are the figures of Humility and Chastity.

In the lower corners are the prophets Micah (?) and Isaiah holding banderoles with inscriptions which may be read: *Do-minus egredietur de loco sancto suo. Isaias XXVI* (The Lord cometh forth out of his holy place. Isaiah 26) and *Parvulus*

FIG. 79. ASTROLOGERS OF THE EAST; THE VISION OF THE MAGI
DETAIL FROM A TAPESTRY FROM BURGOS CATHEDRAL
FLEMISH (BRUSSELS), ABOUT 1500
PROBABLY FROM THE WORKSHOPS OF PIETER VAN AELST

*natus est nobis. Isaias IX* (Unto us a child is born. Isaiah 9).
As the words of the first inscription, except *sancto,* are identical in Isaiah 26.21 and Micah 1.3, the text was probably intended to be a quotation from Micah rather than Isaiah and an identification of the figure as that prophet.

THE VIRGIN AND CHILD is a late mediaeval statue, said to have come from a nunnery in Champagne. The Virgin is not conventionalized as were the Virgins of the thirteenth and fourteenth centuries, but is naturalistically portrayed as one of the ladies of the day; and the lively Infant, unlike earlier, more mannered representations, is a playful, realistic child.

# THE SPANISH ROOM

NUMEROUS indeed are the painted ceilings referred to as Spanish in American private homes and public buildings, but there are few authentic Gothic ceilings, even in Spain. A fine Gothic ceiling dating from the fifteenth century is in the Spanish Room (fig. 80). The ceiling probably came from a *palacio* at Illescas, the halfway stopping place between Madrid and Toledo. It is reported to have been removed from a bedroom occupied by Francis I in 1526 when he was held a prisoner by Charles V. The story is told on good authority. It is impossible, however, to substantiate the claim, for the town of Illescas was completely demolished in the recent revolution.

The ceiling is related to the late fourteenth-century ceiling covering the cloister walk of the monastery of Santo Domingo de Silos, though the latter is simpler in construction. The beams and paneling of both ceilings are similarly arranged, and both ceilings are of red pine coated with a thin gesso foundation and painted. The lower frieze of The Cloisters ceiling was later repainted with animal motives, which resemble closely those of the beams and frieze at Silos.

In The Cloisters ceiling the colors are subdued red, blue, dark green, gray-green, yellow-ocher, brown, black, white, and orange, contrasted with the gold of the rope molding. This palette is well suited to architectural woodwork. Interlacing stems bearing fruits and crisply curving leaves, painted in shades of brown or neutralized green, cover most of the ceiling, including the three master beams and the upper frieze board. The hunting scenes in the lower frieze are repeated in groups of four. Two unidentified coats of arms, used alternately, separate the groups. One shield bears a gold ox or bull in a red field, within a border of gold charged with eight blue taus.

It is upheld by two nude, winged putti (partly restored). The other shield shows a gold castle with three towers, the middle one highest, in a blue field, within a border of gold charged with eight blue crossed keys. Supporting the shield are two parti-colored animals.

The modern stone windows—the capitals alone are original—were designed after a window in the Episcopal Palace in Barcelona, which was destroyed during the recent revolution. A somewhat similar window appears in the retable of Saint John the Baptist in the adjoining Late Gothic Hall (see fig. 83).

THE BRONZE CHANDELIER hanging from the ceiling must have been used to light the home of a wealthy family—for candles were a luxury—in the north of Europe. This lighting fixture was cast in separate pieces; each arm has assembly marks corresponding with marks on the central shaft. The entire surface was hand tooled and the rough parts made smooth before the final polishing. A similar fifteenth-century chandelier is shown in the portrait of Jan Arnolfini and his wife painted by Jan Van Eyck in 1434.

While contemporary paintings and illuminated manuscripts give the best complete picture of domestic interiors in the Middle Ages The Cloisters collection includes a number of fine examples of mediaeval woodwork and furniture. The wood paneling in the Treasury, a few rare examples of Gothic furniture in various galleries, and a number of exhibits in this room illustrate the styles current in the late Middle Ages and show the construction and both the simple and the elaborate carving employed by the early cabinetmaker.

FIG. 80. THE SPANISH ROOM

# THE LATE GOTHIC HALL

FROM the standpoint of its architecture the Late Gothic Hall might be considered the refectory of The Cloisters. The timbered ceiling of this hall, made with hand-worked beams taken from old Connecticut buildings, is in the style of some late mediaeval examples. The fifteenth-century windows are four of the six which were originally in the refectory of the convent of the Dominicans at Sens (see fig. 86). All the windows were probably glazed, and records of the convent show that in the sixteenth century at least one window was filled with stained and painted glass. Three of the four late mediaeval limestone doorways are unusually fine and well preserved (see fig. 81). In the late Middle Ages, as in the late stages of other periods, there was a tendency to exaggerate and make stilted the earlier vocabulary. Although complicated moldings and details are emphasized, these doorways are structurally logical in their ornamentation as well as in their form.

THE PULPIT could have been used in a refectory, where it was customary to have a monk read aloud during meals; however, many such pulpits were used in churches. This piece of furniture is distinctly mediaeval in style, notwithstanding its late date, 1554; the steps are modern.

THE RETABLES, or altarpieces, brought together in this hall are unusual examples of Spanish painting. Such works rivaled in splendor the lavish tombs of the Middle Ages. From the fourteenth century through the late mediaeval period and the Renaissance, retables became more and more numerous and increased in size. They rose impressively, high above the main altars, and they were also used in subordinate chapels,

# THE RETABLES

These altarpieces, unlike portable shrines, were architectural ensembles related to the space around them. Generally Spanish retables were higher than they were broad, and were not provided with folding wings. Like great billboards, they had a story to tell, and the bigger their proportions, the more easily the scenes could be read. The usual arrangement included a large central panel and numerous smaller ones depicting scenes related to the principal subject. Ordinarily the predella, or bottom member of the retable, illustrated other anecdotes. The scenes were colorful, realistic, and elaborated in great detail. In the fourteenth century Spanish painting was influenced by the Sienese and other Italian schools; in the fifteenth century Flemish influences predominated.

FIG. 81. DOORWAY
FRENCH
EARLY XVI CENTURY

The retable with Saint Andrew and scenes from his life, probably by a follower of Borrassá or of the Master of Saint George, is a complete and typical example of Catalan painting of the first half of the fifteenth century. It is painted in tempera on wood panels, and conventionalized oak leaves enrich the framework. The central panel with Saint Andrew enthroned is surmounted by a panel with the Virgin and Child, Saint Catherine, Saint Mary Magdalene, and angels. At the left are panels depicting the calling

FIG. 82. THE BAPTISM OF CHRIST
DETAIL FROM FIGURE 83

of Saint Andrew and the punishment of a wicked mother, who was killed by fire from heaven in Saint Andrew's presence. At the right are the crucifixion of Saint Andrew and Saint Andrew saving a bishop from the devil disguised as a fair woman. In the predella are shown, from left to right, Saint Andrew and the woman who prayed to Diana on behalf of her sister; the woman bringing the saint to her sister; Saint Andrew driving away devils which had taken the form of dogs; the Man of Sorrows; Saint Andrew raising a dead youth; and Saint Andrew bringing to life drowned men.

The painting with scenes from the life of Saint John the Baptist is made up of panels which have now been cleaned and

FIG. 83. RETABLE WITH SCENES FROM
THE LIFE OF SAINT JOHN THE BAPTIST. SPANISH, ABOUT 1480
PROBABLY BY FRANCISCO SOLIBES DE BAÑOLAS

put together to form a retable such as they must once have composed (fig. 83). No attempt has been made to reconstruct the carved and gilded canopies which would originally have been placed over the individual scenes, and only simple moldings, consistent with old moldings on the predella, have been used for the framework. A Crucifixion scene, with the swooning Virgin supported by Saint John and two holy women, and with four men casting lots for the seamless garment of Christ, surmounts the entire composition. The large central panel represents Saint John seated on a throne; in his raised left hand he holds his attribute, the book with the Lamb of God upon it. The smaller panels, beginning in the upper left-hand corner and continuing in each register from left to right, depict the following scenes from the saint's life: the angel appearing to Zacharias, the father of John the Baptist; the Visitation of the Virgin Mary to Elisabeth; the birth of John the Baptist; his preaching beside the Jordan; his baptism of Christ (fig. 82); his reproval of Herod; and his beheading and the presentation of his head to Herodias.

The predella consists of two parts, each composed of three panels with paintings of saints. Carved and gilded arcading above and crocketed columns at the sides frame the individual panels in such a way as to create niches for the saints. A central panel now used for the label was originally intended either for another painting or more probably for a small carved and gilded wood tabernacle, in which the Host was kept. The panels, from left to right, represent Saint Martial (inscribed Sant Marcal), Saint Sebastian (Sant Sabastia), Saint Mary Magdalene (Santa Mag), Saint Bridget (Santa Brigida), Saint Christopher, carrying the Christ Child (without inscription), and Saint Kilian (Sant Quilez [Quilenus]).

In all the compositions the figures predominate, the architecture and the landscape of the backgrounds being secondary. The expressiveness of the faces contrasts sharply with the woodenness of the figures, which are garbed in almost schematic late Gothic draperies. The costumes are painted in gay, lively colors. Crimson and vermilion, grass green, white, and patches of yellow stand out among the softer tones of olive drab, purple, deep blue, and a variety of other shades. Several of the garments, especially those of Zacharias, and the bed coverlet in the scene of the birth of Saint John are richly patterned in gold, as are other details. The whole effect is sumptuous. In striking contrast is the ascetic costume of Saint John. Tones of gray are employed chiefly for the buildings, against which the bright figures are silhouetted. Certain details are stressed by the juxtaposition of contrasting colors, as for instance in the Baptism, where God the Father with his gold halo is looking down from a yellow orb surrounded by concentric bands of red and blue.

The central panel of the retable of Saint John the Baptist is like the incomplete retable with three large panels representing Saint Isidore, Saint Ambrose, and Saint Nicholas which is in the collegiate church of Santa María de Calatayud in the province of Saragossa, and has an almost identical predella. Both retables, however, must be compared to the great retable in the chapel of the Piedad at San Llorens dels Morunys, which according to accepted documents was "painted" on July 17, 1480, by Francisco Solibes de Bañolas. In all probability all three retables were painted by this master, a Catalan who may have worked in Aragon.

The predella of another large retable depicts six scenes from the Passion—the Agony in the Garden; the Betrayal of Christ; Christ before Caiaphas; Christ crowned with thorns; the Flagellation of Christ; and Christ before Pilate—with heads of apostles (Peter, Andrew, James the Greater, Thomas, Bartholomew, and Matthew) in medallions below. It has been

147

ascribed to various Aragonese painters of the second half of the fifteenth century.

The largest of the retables (fig. 84), its principal panel representing Saint Anne with the Virgin and Child, is over fifteen feet high. Saint Anne is seated on an elaborate Gothic throne on which there are niches with Adam and Eve and figures, probably angels, with musical instruments. In the panel above is shown the Crucifixion, with Christ and the two thieves, the Virgin, the three Marys, and Saint John the Evangelist. At the left are the Virgin of the Rosary, standing in a mandorla of flames, with four angels playing musical instruments and, above, the miracle in which, according to legend, a gentleman of Cologne, who had killed a friend in a quarrel, was saved from the vengeance of the victim's brother by the Virgin, who placed a garland of roses on his head as he kneeled before her altar. At the right are Saint Michael, weighing two souls and trampling a demon symbolizing Satan, and, above, Saint Michael's miracle at Monte Gargano. In this version Dominican monks followed by a pope, two cardinals, bishops, nobles, and ladies lead the way to the cave where a bull indicates the site for a church. The predella shows Joachim and Anne expelled from the temple; their meeting at the Golden Gate; the Mass of Saint Gregory; the birth of the Virgin; and her presentation in the temple. On the dust guards (*guardapolvos*) are angels bearing instruments of the Passion.

This retable, from a monastery at Teruel, was painted in the second half of the fifteenth century. The original text of the inscription may be read as follows: . . . *An fecho fazer los muy onrados Mosén Miguel Armisén i Atón Incet en el anyo de mi[l]* CCCC [LXXXIII] (The most honorable Mosén Miguel Armisén and Atón Incet have caused [it] to be made in the year 14[83]). Unfortunately the raised gold letters at the two ends have been restored, and the date is therefore uncertain.

FIG. 84. RETABLE WITH SAINT ANNE AND THE VIRGIN AND CHILD
SPANISH (ARAGONESE), SECOND HALF OF THE XV CENTURY

THE SCULPTURES. The life-size figures of the three kings, Caspar, Balthasar, and Melchior, were carved about 1490 as part of an Adoration group that once formed the central section of the retable of the high altar of the convent of Lichtenthal in Baden, Germany. The Virgin and Child from the group remains at the convent. The painted wings of the

FIG. 85. THE VIRGIN KNEELING
ITALIAN, EARLY XVI CENTURY

retable were recently exhibited at Karlsruhe. These figures of the three kings recall the work of the Ulm sculptor Jörg Syrlin the Younger, and the morris dancers by Erasmus Grasser in the old City Hall in Munich.

The early sixteenth-century statue of a kneeling Virgin from a Nativity group (fig. 85) continues the tradition of Central Italian mediaeval wood carving. Strictly speaking, this is a renaissance work, but as it has long been in The Cloisters collection and is reminiscent of earlier wood carving it is exhibited here.

It is related to a group of wood sculptures, including a Virgin at Chieti, a Virgin and Child at Teramo, and similar groups in the Museo civico at Aquila. It is attributed to Gagliardelli, of whom little is known, except that he lived at Città Sant' Angelo and at Chieti and practiced painting as well as sculpture. He contracted to do a group of the Virgin and Child for Santa Maria Magna in Ripatransone in 1524 and painted a fresco for the same church in 1526.

150

# THE SCULPTURES

The painted wood statue of Saint Roch, also a sixteenth-century work, is said to have come from Cherbourg, in the north of France. There are many stories told about Saint Roch. One concerns an incident that is alleged to have taken place when the Council of Constance was about to be adjourned in 1414, owing to the plague. According to tradition, the plague came to an end when, at the suggestion of a young German monk, who had traveled in France and there had heard wondrous tales of Saint Roch, the council ordered an effigy of the saint to be carried in a procession through the streets.

## THE PASCHAL CANDLESTICK.

A special very large candlestick was required in the Middle Ages, as today, for the celebration of the Easter festival. On Easter Eve a large paschal candle, placed in the candlestick, was solemnly blessed and ceremoniously lighted from newly-kindled fire to symbolize the glory of Christ's resurrection. The candle was afterwards relighted for all services of the church for at least the forty days between Easter and the Feast of the Ascension. Easter candlesticks were sometimes of wax like the candles, sometimes of bronze or precious metals, sometimes of wood or stone. The Cloisters candlestick is of wood, painted and gilded; it is six feet five inches in height and is constructed in the form of a hexagonal shaft tapering at the top. Against backgrounds of tooled gold are three bands of figures painted in tones of leaf green, salmon, olive gray, and vermilion. In the upper tier are six personages of the Old Law, in the middle tier six saints, and in the bottom register six apostles. These paintings have been related to the work of Jorge Inglés, who painted the Retable of the Angels for the chapel of the hospital at Buitrago south of Burgos in Castile in the second half of the fifteenth century.

FIG. 86. A VIEW OF THE CLOISTERS
SHOWING TWO WINDOWS FROM SENS AND THE FROVILLE ARCADE

# THE FROVILLE ARCADE

THE exterior of the entrance passageway along the upper driveway is formed by nine pointed, cusped arches from the fifteenth-century cloister of the Benedictine priory of Froville (see fig. 86). The arches are placed on a parapet in groups of three and separated by buttresses, as they were at Froville.

Arcades of this type were frequently employed in fourteenth- and fifteenth-century cloisters, for they permitted solid construction and did not require great ingenuity of the artist or particular skill of the stonecutter, as did the more elaborately carved Romanesque and early Gothic cloister arcades. By the end of the Middle Ages arcades were in most instances treated as a series of windows. In the Renaissance and later periods cloisters derived their impressiveness from their proportions rather than from the decoration of the architecture.

The original cloister at Froville was located on the north side of the church, near the tower. It had a small, square court with nine arches on each side. Over the cloister walk there was a second story, a stringcourse above the arches indicating the floor level. The rubble walls were originally plastered, and it is possible that even the stone arches were covered. It has been suggested that the tool marks were left on the surface of the stone so that the plaster would adhere.

A document of the year 1091 records that a nobleman named Odouin gave the church and other properties to the Benedictine abbey of Cluny, and thus the priory of Froville was founded. The priory suffered during the Thirty Years' War (1618-1648). In 1791 it was confiscated and sold by the state and the property was used as a farm. One side of the cloister was still standing in 1920; the other sides were demolished before 1904 to make room for the building of stables.

FIG. 87. THE VIEW OF THE HUDSON RIVER AND THE
GEORGE WASHINGTON BRIDGE FROM THE CLOISTERS. IN THE FOREGROUND
IS THE GARDEN COURT OF THE BONNEFONT CLOISTER

# INDEX

This index is confined mainly to objects in The Cloisters collections and to the names of persons and places related to them. The objects are indexed under such categories as Architecture, Metalwork, Paintings, Sculpture. Only the first mention of a subject in a chapter is listed.

Abbeville, 98
Aelst, Pieter van, 135
Albigensian heretics, xx, 16
Albret, Jean d', 86
Alençon, 133
Alexander the Great, 48
Alluye, Jean d', v, 65
Amboise, Jacques d', 100
Anne of Brittany, xxi, 120, 128
Antioch, viii, 102
Aragonese objects of art. *See* Spanish objects of art
Architecture
  Abaci. *See* Chapter house from Notre-Dame-de-Pontaut; Choir; Cloisters
  Arcades. *See* Cloisters
  Arches: fragment from Larreule, 85; from Narbonne, 46. *See also below* Chapter house from Notre-Dame-de-Pontaut; Choir; Cloisters
  Canopies, 74
  Capitals: from the ciborium at Saint-Michel-de-Cuxa, 44; [Spanish], 140. *See also below* Chapter house from Notre-Dame-de-Pontaut; Choir; Cloisters; Doorway; Fountains
  Ceilings: from Illescas, vii, 139; from the Tyrol, 119
  Chapter house from Notre-Dame-de-Pontaut, vi, xviii, xxxi, 33
  Choir, elements of, from the church at Langon, vii, xxviii, xxxi, 22
  Ciborium, 26
  Cloisters, elements of: from Bonnefont-en-Comminges, v, xxviii, xxxi, 81, 86; from Froville, vii, xxviii, xxxi, 153; from Saint-Guilhem-le-Désert, v, xxviii, xxxi, 16, 25; from

Saint-Michel-de-Cuxa, v, xxviii, xxxi, 38; from Trie, v, vii, xxxi, 85
  Columns: from Notre-Dame-de-la-Grande-Sauve, 21. *See also above* Chapter house from Notre-Dame-de-Pontaut; Choir; Cloisters. *See also below* Doorways
  Corbels: from Notre-Dame-de-la-Grande-Suave, 21; twelfth-century, vii
  Doors: [wood, thirteenth-century], 32. *See also* Sculpture; Woodwork
  Doorways: from Beaune, 1; from Frías, vii, 44; from Gimont, 65; from Moutiers-Saint-Jean, vi, xxxii, 11; from Reugny, vii, 6; from southwest France, 1; incorporated in the building xxxi; [late] Gothic, 119; late mediaeval, 142
  Fountains: from Figeac, 21; from Notre-Dame-du-Vilar, 46; from Saint-Genis-des-Fontaines, 46; late fifteenth- or early sixteenth-century, 89. *See also below* Lavabo
  Lavabo, 46
  Mantelpiece from Alençon, 133
  Windows: from Beaumont-le-Roger, 63; from Cluny, 133; from la Tricherie, 63; from Sens, vii, 142; incorporated in the building, xxxi
Armengol VII, Count of Urgel, v, 67
Armengol X, Count of Urgel, 67
Arthur, King, 48
Aumale, 73
Austrian objects of art, 79
Autun, 27

155

Baden, 150
Barnard, George Gray, v, 18
Bartolo di Fredi, 63
Bataille, Nicolas, 51
Beaumont-le-Roger, 63
Beaune, 1
Berry, Jean, Duke of, 50
Bertinus, 104
Blumenthal, George, vii
Bonnefont Cloister, v, xxxiv, 81
Bonnefont-en-Comminges, v, xxviii, xxxi, 81, 86
Boppard, 115
Boppard Room, 115
Borrassá, a follower of, 143
Bourges, 52
Brummer, Joseph, viii
Burgos, 135
Burgos Tapestry Hall, 135
Burgundian objects of art. See French objects of art
Burgundy, xviii, 14, 90

Cabrera, Don Alvaró de, 67
Caesar, Julius, 48
Candlesticks. See Metalwork; Paintings
Catalan objects of art. See under Spanish objects of art
Catherine, Queen of Navarre, 86
Cerezo de Riotirón, vi, xxxii, 3
Chalices. See Metalwork
Channel School, 107
Charlemagne, xvii, xxxv, 16
Charles, Prince (later the Emperor Charles V), 133, 139
Charles VI [of France], 50
Charles VIII [of France], 120
Church, The, xxii
Ciborium. See Architecture; Metalwork
Cione, a follower of Nardo di, 62
Clark, Stephen Carlton, vii, 85
Clovis and Clothar, 11
Cluny, 133; abbey of, xxvi, 28
Constantine, 99
Crucifix. See Sculpture
Cuxa Cloister, xx, 38

David, 48
Dulcia, Doña, [Countess of Urgel], 67

Early Christian objects of art, 102
Early Gothic Hall, 56
Ebreichsdorf, 79
Eleanor of Aquitaine, xx, 24
Enamels. See Metalwork
Évron, 77

Ferdinand of Aragon, xxii, 135
Fifteenth-Century Sculpture Hall, 65, 90
Figeac, 21
Flemish objects of art: vi, 95, 100, 102, 133, 135, 140; Franco-Flemish, vi, 120
Florence, 62, 63
Francis I, 98, 120, 125, 139
Franco-Flemish objects of art, vi, 120
Frederick II, 112
Freiburg in Breisgau, 105
French objects of art: v, vi, vii, viii, 6, 8, 16, 21, 22, 32, 33, 38, 44, 46, 47, 61, 63, 65, 73, 76, 77, 81, 85, 92, 98, 100, 108, 133, 142, 151; from Burgundy, vi, xxxii, 1, 11, 27, 46, 76, 90, 91, 133; from Champagne, 94, 138; from the Île-de-France, v, vi, 58, 92; from Limoges, 110, 111, 112; from Lorraine, v, 89, 108, 153; Meuse, from the region of the, 112. See also Channel School; Franco-Flemish objects of art; Rhenish objects of art
Frescoes: by a follower of Nardo di Cione, 62; from San Pedro de Arlanza, vi, 1
Frías, vii, 44
Froville, vii, xxviii, xxxi, 153
Furniture: 140; pulpit, 142

Gagliardelli, 150
Gardens, xxxiv, 83
German objects of art, 95, 96, 105, 111, 112, 114, 118, 150. See also Rhenish objects of art
Gimont, 65
Ginestarre de Cardós, 26
Gothic Chapel, 65
Greiff, Hans, 113
Guilhem, Duke of Aquitaine, 16

# INDEX

Hall of the Unicorn Tapestries, 120
Henry, Count of Nassau, 133
Henry II of England, xvi, 24
Hugo, Brother, of Oignies, 108

Illescas, vii, 139
Ingolstadt, 113
Isabella of Castile, xxii, 135
Italian objects of art, v, 9, 26, 61, 62, 63, 93, 112, 150

Joanna, wife of Philip the Fair, 135
Joshua, 48
Juan, Pedro. See Pedro Juan
Jumièges, 100

la Celle, 61
la Clarté-Dieu, 65
Langon, vii, xxviii, xxxi, 22
La Rochefoucauld, François de, 120
Larreule, 85
Late Gothic Hall, 142
la Tricherie, 63
Lavaudieu, 8
Leatherwork, shoe reliquary, 108
Leinberger, Hans, 119
Lichtenthal, 150
Limoges, 110
Longroy, Clément de, 73
Longuyon, Jacques de, 48
Louis XII, 120, 128

Maria-Strassengel, 79
Master of Saint George, a follower of, 143
Maximilian, 133, 135
Metalwork
  Bronzes: aquamaniles, 111; bird, 112; chandelier, 140; clasp, 112
  Copper-gilt [reliquary] figure, 108
  Enamels: altar candlesticks, 110; basins (gemellions), 111; cruet, 110; eucharistic dove, 110; flabellum, 108
  Silver: beakers, 113, chalice, paten, and straws, 105; chalice by Bertinus, 104; chalice of Antioch, viii, 102; ciborium, bowl from, 106; reliquary arm, 108

Metalwork, continued
  Wrought-iron door mountings, 100
Middle Ages in France and Spain, The, xvii
Monastery, The, xxvii
Monasticism, xxiii
Monticchio, 61
Morgan, J. Pierpont, 117
Moutiers-Saint-Jean, vi, xxxii, 11
Mur, Don Dalmau de, 118

Narbonne, 46
Nardo di Cione, follower of, 62
Netherlandish objects of art, 95. See also Flemish objects of art
Niccoló di Tommaso, 63
Nine Heroes Tapestry Room, 47
Notre-Dame-de-la-Grande-Sauve, xxviii, 21, 22
Notre-Dame-de-Pontaut, vi, xxviii, xxxi, 33
Notre-Dame-du-Vilar, 46

Oignies, Brother Hugo of, 108
Orcagna, follower of, 63

Paintings: Adoration of the Shepherds, by Bartolo di Fredi, 63; altarpiece by a follower of Van der Weyden, 101; Intercession of Christ and the Virgin, 63; paschal candlestick, 151; predella with scenes from the Passion, 147; retable of Saint Andrew, 143; retable of Saint Anne with the Virgin and Child, 148; retable of Saint John the Baptist, probably by Solibes de Bañolas, 140, 144. See also Frescoes
Pedro Juan, 118
Philip the Fair, 133, 135
Pons, Beatrice de, 73

Ranucius, Nicolaus, and sons Giovanni and Guitonne, 27
Reliquaries, 107
Reugny, vii, 6
Rhenish objects of art, 92, 108; from Boppard, 115; from Strasbourg, viii, 56

Rockefeller, John D., Jr., v, viii, 122
Romanesque Chapel, vii, 22
Romanesque Hall, 1, 34
Roussillon, xx
Rule of Saint Benedict, xxiv-xxvi, xxviii

Saint Benedict of Aniane, xxv, 16
Saint Benedict of Nursia, xxiv, xxviii
Saint-Genis-des-Fontaines, 46
Saint-Guilhem Cloister, v, 16
Saint-Guilhem-le-Désert, v, xxviii, xxxi, 16, 25
Saint-Léonard-de-Noblac, 100
Saint Martha, atelier of, 94
Saint-Michel-de-Cuxa, v, xxviii, xxxi, xxxii, 37, 38, 44
S[ain]t-Omer, 104
Saint Trudpert, 105
San Pedro de Arlanza, vi, 1
Santa Clara, 28
Santa Maria de Bellpuig de las Avellanas, 67, 76
Santo Stefano, 27
Saragossa, 117
Sculptures: Adoration of the Magi, vi, xxxii, 3, for figures from another Adoration group, see three kings below; altar frontal, 25; angels, 76; bishop, Burgundian, 76; bishop, from Monticchio, 61; bishop with a donor, Burgundian, 91; burgher, 91; Clovis and Clothar [Frankish kings], 11; crucifix, vii, 28; deacon saint, 61; head of Christ, 94; holy women, 94; Madonna and Child, 93; panels, wood, with scenes from the Life of Christ, 100; Pietà, French, 92; Pietà, Rhenish, 92; relief of the lion of Judah, vii, 10; relief with Saint Hubert and the stag, 94; retable from Saragossa, 117; Saint Barbara, 92; Saint Denis, 91; Saint James the Greater, 46, 91; Saint John, v, 9; Saint Margaret, 74; Saint Roch, 151; Saint Stephen, attributed to Leinberger, 118; stations of the Cross, 89; three kings from an Adoration group, 150;

tomb of Armengol VII, Count of Urgel, v, 67; tomb of Armengol X, Count of Urgel, 67; tomb of Don Alvaró de Cabrera, 67; tomb of Doña Dulcia, [Countess of Urgel], 67; tomb effigy of Jean d'Alluye, v, 65; tomb slab of Clément de Longroy and his wife, 73; torso of Christ, v, 6; unidentified female saint, 74; Virgin, from the Île-de-France, v, from Lorraine, v, from Strasbourg Cathedral, viii, 56, thirteenth-century, v, 9; Virgin and Child, from Autun (?), 27, from Champagne, 138, from the Île-de-France, vi, 58; Virgin kneeling, attributed to Gagliardelli, 150. See also Architecture
Sens, vii, 142
Sluter, Claus, 90
Solibes de Bañolas, Francisco, 147
Spanish objects of art: v, vii, xxxii, 1, 3, 10, 28, 44, 139, 151; Aragonese, 147, 148; Catalan, v, viii, 25, 67, 74, 100, 117, 140, 143, 144
Spanish Room, 139
Stained glass: from Austria, panels with Saint Bartholomew, Saint John the Evangelist, and Saint Martin and the beggar, 79; from Boppard, panels with Saint Barbara, Saint Catherine of Alexandria, Saint Dorothea of Caesarea, the Virgin with ears of wheat on her robe, and bishop saints, 115; from Ebreichsdorf, quatrefoil and panel with the Annunciation, 79; from Évron, panels with Isaiah and Mary Magdalene, 77; from Maria-Strassengel, panel with the Virgin of the Mantel, 79; from Sulz am Neckar, panels portraying Wilhelm von Weitingen and his wife, with their heraldic arms, 96; from Troyes, panels with Christ (?) and an apostle (?), the Virgin (?) and a monk, a bishop and a kneeling man, and figures from an Adoration scene, 31-32; panels with the arms of Maximilian,

# INDEX

Philip the Fair, Prince Charles, Henry, Count of Nassau, and Roland Le Febure, 133; roundels, German, Netherlandish, Swiss, 95
Strasbourg, viii, 56
Sulz am Neckar, 96
Swiss objects of art, 95

Tapestries: Hunt of the Unicorn, The, vii, xxxiv, 120; Nativity, The, 135; Nine Heroes, The, viii, 47
Teruel, 148
Treasury, The, viii, 99
Trie, v, vii, xxxi, 85
Trie Cloister, v, vii, 85
Troyes, 32, 94

Tyrol, 119
Tyrolese objects of art, 119

Urgel, 67

Vaglia Mugello, 94
Verdun, Nicholas of, 111
Verteuil, 120

Weitingen, Wilhelm von, 96
Weyden, van der, follower of, 101
Witiza. *See* Saint Benedict of Aniane
Woodwork: 140; from Abbeville, 98.
    *See also* Architecture; Sculpture

Zamora, vii, 10
Zimmern, Barbara von, 96

THIS BOOK WAS FIRST PUBLISHED IN MAY MCMXXXVIII.
OF THIS THE ELEVENTH EDITION, EXTENSIVELY REVISED
AND ENLARGED, TWENTY THOUSAND COPIES WERE
PRINTED IN JUNE MCMLI BY THE PLANTIN PRESS,
NEW YORK

A SECOND IMPRESSION OF TWENTY THOUSAND COPIES,
WITH MINOR CHANGES, WAS PRINTED IN JUNE MCMLIII

A THIRD IMPRESSION OF TWENTY THOUSAND COPIES,
WITH MINOR CHANGES, WAS PRINTED IN JUNE MCMLV


THE TOTAL NUMBER OF COPIES PRINTED TO DATE IS
ONE HUNDRED AND SIXTY-SIX THOUSAND